NA ITS NO ITS ONLY GLESCA
AMERICA!!
IF TWO MEN
IN 3 DAYS
WHATS A' THIS
KT-433-382

MAW— GIE'S AN EGG. I WANT TAE ROLL IT DOON THE WHINNEY DEN!
WEEL, THERE'S ONLY ANE LEFT, AN' IT'S AN AWFY JOB TAE GET EGGS—BUT YE CAN HAE IT! I'LL DYE IT AN' BOIL IT FOR THE MORN!
HULLO, SOAPY. I'M AWA' TAE ROLL MA EGG!
THERE'S THE WHINNEY DEN—WE'LL ROLL IT THERE!
WE'LL ROLL IT DOON HERE, SYNE I'LL EAT IT!
AW, BUT WE SHOULD GET A BITTIE.
WHA'S EGG IS IT ONYWEY?
WEEL, BE FAIR, WE SHOULD DRAW LOTS FOR IT, OR RAFFLE IT!
AYE!
BY JINGS! IF IT ISNA' BROON! YE MIND WHEN WE WERE LADDIES THEGITHER FIFTY YEARS SYNE?
CRIVVENS! ALEC ANDERSON. I LAST SAW YE WHEN YE LEFT THE SCHULE AN' WENT TAE WORK IN PERTH!
MEBBE HE'S LEAVIN' US FOR EVER!
CAN WE COME TOO MAW?
MINISTERS
8, 1945.
LEE CHOOSES HIS
OR KEY POSTS
EVIN FOR FOREIGN OFFICE
Chancellor
OF LORDS

King George VI.

Prime Minister, Clement Attlee.

THE years 1936 to 1946 saw an intense amount of change in the world. A period dominated by World War 2 saw Britain governed by four Prime Ministers and ruled by three Kings. The Broons and Oor Wullie also changed from their first appearances in 1936, evolving into the iconic figures recognised by millions today. But all through this turbulent time The Broons and Oor Wullie never changed from their aim of delivering family fun every week.

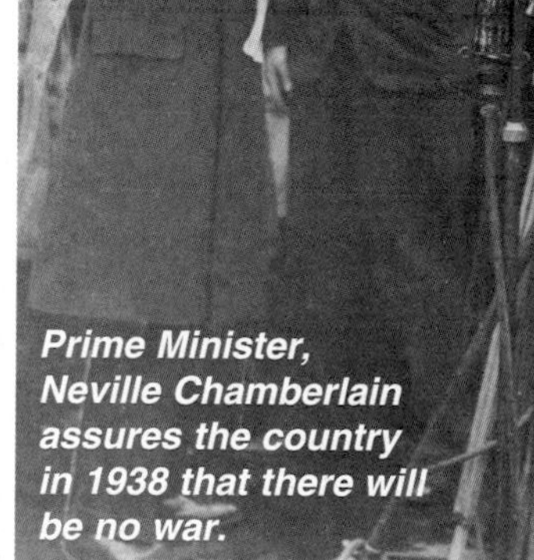

Prime Minister, Neville Chamberlain assures the country in 1938 that there will be no war.

Prime Minister, Winston Churchill.

The archive nature of the enclosed material means that image quality may vary slightly on some pages while some pages contain references which are of their time which would not be considered acceptable today.

Printed and Published in Great Britain by DC Thomson & Co., Ltd.
185 Fleet Street, London, EC4A 2HS.

ISBN 1 84535 162 2

1936

ARE YE MINDING THE MORN'S THE DAY FOR WULLIE LINDSAY'S WEDDING? WHAUR'S THE INVITE?— I'VE LOST IT!
WELL, I KEN ITS ON FRIDAY AT 7·30!
APRIL 2nd THURS
BANG! YOU'RE DEID
APRIL 3rd FRI
BEAUTIFUL!! HUH!
COME ON PAW GET READY NOO!
YE MAUN BE CLEAN FOR THE WEDDIN'
OCH! I DINNA WANT TAE GANG
SOAP
NOW STAY THERE TILL I'M READY
CLEANLINESS
I SUPPOSE I'LL NEED TO SHAVE
NA, ITS OWER DEAR
WILL WE GET A TAXI?
WHAUR'S THE BAIRN?
AM I ALRIGHT MAW?
OH-!!??
MAW, YE HAV'NA PRESSED MA BREEKS!
MERCY ME!!
MAW, PAW'S LOST HIS COLLAR STUD-OW!!
MAYBE ITS UNDER THE PIANO?
I'VE GOT SOME COAL!
NOW WE'RE OFF
PAW, TAK YER HAUNDS OOT'N YER POCKETS!
WHA'T A SICHT!
AW SWANK!
HALL FOR WEDDINGS FUNERALS PARTIES PIE-EATING CONTESTS DIDDLING COMPETITIONS
WULLIE LINDSAY'S WEDDING? YE'RE OWER SUNE— IT'S NEXT FRIDAY!

The Sunday Post 5th April 1936

OOR WULLIE 1936-1946

I'M AYE FED UP THESE DAYS!
MIND THIS EASTER EGG WHILE I GO IN HERE
TO BE DELIVERED
TO BE DELIVERED
BE DELIVERED
TO BE DELIVERED
CLICK
BE DELIVERED

The Sunday Post 12th April 1936

HERE'S A LETTER FRAE AUNTIE JEAN IN AUCHENTOGLE INVITIN' MAGGIE, DAPHNE & ME UP FOR SUNDAY!
THAT'LL BE A'RICHT MAW, WE'LL MIND THE HOOSE!
WE'RE AWA' THEN PAW! WE'VE LEFT THE HOOSE A' NICE & TIDY FOR YE!
A'RICHT MAW HAVE A GUID TIME!
THIS IS GRAUND
FOOTBALL NEWS
THIS MAKS A FINE HAMMOCK
ROVER
SNORE
ITS TWEL' O'CLOCK, TIME WE WERE UP
I'D BETTER PUT MAIR SALT IN THE PORRIDGE
CAN YE DAE THIS?
I'M PLAYIN AT HOOSES
I'M GOING TO HAVE PINEAPPLES FOR BREAKFAST
OW!
PONG!
?
WOW! MAW'S BEST JUG
GOOD JOB THE CHIP SHOP WAS OPEN!
CALL THIS PORRIDGE?
WELL, I PUT HALF A PACKET O' SALT IN IT!!
I'M FEELIN' SICK!
PEARS
JAM
OH, MAGGIE! LOOK AT THE HOOSE!
I'M DEID!
BANG!
SUNDAY POST

The Sunday Post 3rd May 1936

I'M ON THE LOOK OUT FOR HIM WULLIE
MAN WANTED
£50 REWARD FOR CAPTURE
I'D LIKE TAE HAE A SHOTTIE AT GETTING THAT REWARD.
DO NOT PARK CARS HERE WET CEMENT
CEMENT
WHAT ARE YE LOOKIN' AT?
YOU'RE NO' HIM!
THERE HE IS!
GARAGE
PETROL
SIX GALLONS!
IS THERE A CAR PARK NEAR HERE?
YES SIR, JUST ROOND THE CORNER
I'VE GOT IT!
DO NOT
PARK CARS HERE WET CEMENT
HAH! THIS MUST BE THE PARKING PLACE
PARK CARS HERE
NOW I'VE GOT HIM
HOTEL
I'VE GOT THAT WANTED MAN
HOW'D YE MANAGE IT?
HIS CAR'S STUCK IN CEMENT
HA-HA!
QUICK! HE'S GOT MEN TAE BRAK AWA THE CEMENT
THATS NO' HIM — THAT'S THE CHIEF CONSTABLE!

The Sunday Post 20th September 1936

WE'RE GOING TO HAVE A LODGER, OH, HE'S A CHARMING YOUNG MAN!
I'VE FALLEN FOR HIM
HOW DO YOU DO, MRS BROWN?
WELCOME MR. SLICK!
MR. SLICK HAS GOT YOUR BEDROOM, SO YOU'LL SLEEP IN HERE!
I MADE THIS MYSELF!
HE'S GOT PAW'S CHAIR, MY BEST SUIT ON, & SMOKING HEN'S CIGARETTES!
WE'RE LOOKING FOR HARRY SLICK!
HARRY SLICK WANTED FOR FRAUD
SQUASH
REVENGE IS SWEET!
HARRY SLICK WANTED FOR FRAUD

The Sunday Post 17th May 1936

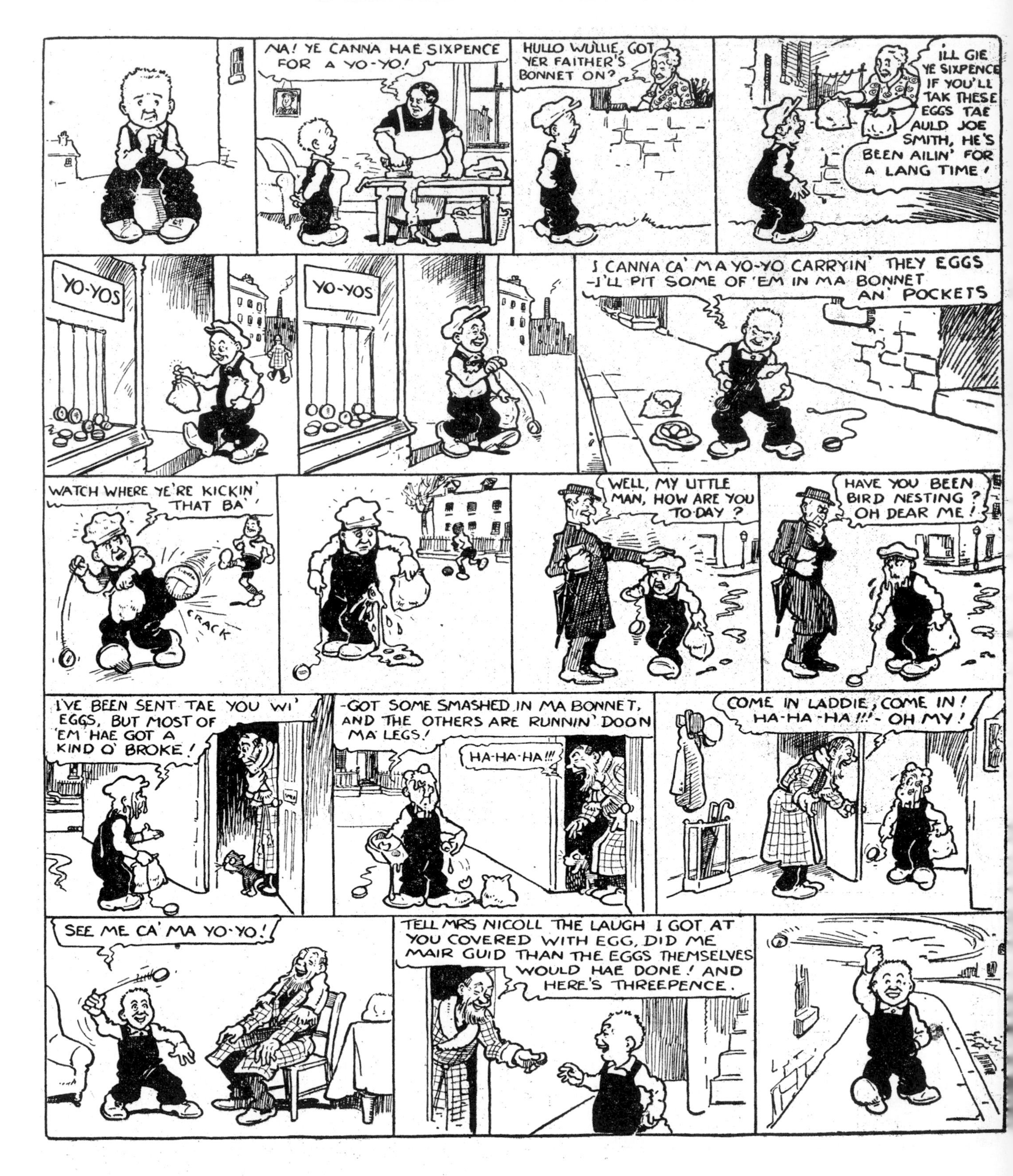
NA! YE CANNA HAE SIXPENCE FOR A YO-YO!
HULLO WULLIE, GOT YER FAITHER'S BONNET ON?
I'LL GIE YE SIXPENCE IF YOU'LL TAK THESE EGGS TAE AULD JOE SMITH, HE'S BEEN AILIN' FOR A LANG TIME!
YO-YOS
YO-YOS
I CANNA CA' MA YO-YO CARRYIN' THEY EGGS —I'LL PIT SOME OF 'EM IN MA BONNET AN' POCKETS
WATCH WHERE YE'RE KICKIN' THAT BA'
CRACK
WELL, MY LITTLE MAN, HOW ARE YOU TO-DAY?
HAVE YOU BEEN BIRD NESTING? OH DEAR ME!
I'VE BEEN SENT TAE YOU WI' EGGS, BUT MOST OF 'EM HAE GOT A KIND O' BROKE!
-GOT SOME SMASHED IN MA BONNET, AND THE OTHERS ARE RUNNIN' DOON MA LEGS!
HA-HA-HA!!!
COME IN LADDIE, COME IN! HA-HA-HA!!!- OH MY!
SEE ME CA' MA YO-YO!
TELL MRS NICOLL THE LAUGH I GOT AT YOU COVERED WITH EGG, DID ME MAIR GUID THAN THE EGGS THEMSELVES WOULD HAE DONE! AND HERE'S THREEPENCE.

The Sunday Post 25th October 1936

LISTEN TO THIS—" SPEND THE WEEK-END AT LOCHSIDE HOSTEL, BEDS PROVIDED, COOK YOUR OWN FOOD" !
I THINK IT WID DAE US A' A WORLD O' GUID TAE GO THIS WEEK END, MAW!
THAT'S NO A BAD IDEA PAW!
THIS WILL BE YOUR TENT MADAM
MICHTY ME! I THOCHT WE WERE GOING TAE SLEEP IN A HOSTEL !!
THIS IS GREAT!
IT'S GEY STORMY! I HOPE THE TENT ROPES HOLD!
ARE YE NO' ASLEEP YET PAW?
OH MY! THATS DONE IT!—AND IT'S RAININ' !!
RUN INTO THIS BUILDING, QUICK!
SNORE

The Sunday Post 12th July 1936

"HOW TO BE A TOUGH GUY, —TRAIN BY RUNNING, WEIGHT LIFTING, JUMPING, BOXING, DEEP BREATHING"
BOXING
FRESH AIR
COUGH-GURGLE
WHIT'S YER HURRY? IT'S EARLY YET!
I'M A TOUGH GUY, I'M TRAINING!
HEY! WHIT ARE YOU DOIN'?
CAN'T CATCH ME HE-HE
I'LL TAK THIS BURN IN MY STRIDE
THAT'S WHIT YE GET WI' EXERCISE!
WULLIE! YER MAW WANTS YE!
THEN COME AND FETCH ME!

The Sunday Post 22nd November 1936

WELL, WE'RE AWA TAE THE MATCH!
MIND NOW PAW, YOU'RE NO' TAE PLAY, YE HURT YERSEL' LAST TIME!
SAY, MR BROON, COULD YE PLAY IN GOAL? OOR GOALIE'S NO' WEEL!
MAW SAID YE WERE'NT TAE PLAY, PAW!
SHURRUP!
D'YE HEAR THAT?
COME AWA! PAW BROON!
CRASH!
BUMP!!
YOU'D TRY YER CLAIRTY TRICKS ON MY PUIR MAN, WOULD YE?

The Sunday Post 1st November 1936

OOR WULLIE 1936-1946

The Sunday Post 6th December 1936

MY FAITHER CAN FIGHT THREE POLICEMEN — I'LL TELL ON YOU!
OOR PAW CAN FIGHT SIX POLICEMEN. WE'LL TELL ON YOU!
HA-HA!! — HOORAY! EXPRESS TRAIN — CH-CH-CH!!
WHISTLE

The Sunday Post 20th December 1936

OOR WULLIE 1936-1946

WULLIE, STAY IN AND MIND THE BAIRN I'VE THE MESSAGES TAE-DAE.
IF THE BAKER COMES, GET TWA LOAVES, AN' A PINT O'MILK FROM THE MILKMAN, IF THE FISHMAN COMES ROOND GET A PAIR O' KIPPERS, IF THE BUTCHER CALLS GET A PUND O' MINCE
WHAT WAS IT? — FOUR LOAVES QUART O' MILK, SIX KIPPERS A ROAST?
NO! THAT'S WRONG! — FIVE LOAVES, QUART AN' A HALF O' MILK, SIX PAIRS O' KIPPERS, A ROAST, A PUND O' SAUSAGES — AN' FOR MERCY'S SAKE SHURRUP YOU!
YELL
ARE YE ENTERTAININ' THE QUINS?
OH YES! I MIND NOW FIVE BOTTLES PLEASE
HEY MISTER! — HALF A DOZEN PAIRS O' KIPPERS AN' A COD!
O.K.
GUID ORDER, SON!
MAW'LL PEY YE WHEN YE'RE ROOND AGAIN!
RACING NEWS
ONY BREAD THE DAY?
AYE! MAW SAID — 'TWA LOAVES, A HAUF PAN, AN' A CURRANT LOAF — I THINK
— A ROAST, PUND O' STAKE AN' A HAUF PUND O' MINCE
IT'S YER MAW WULLIE

The Sunday Post 20th December 1936

AN' JEELY MAW?
DINNA BOTHER ME NOO! I'M OWER BUSY!

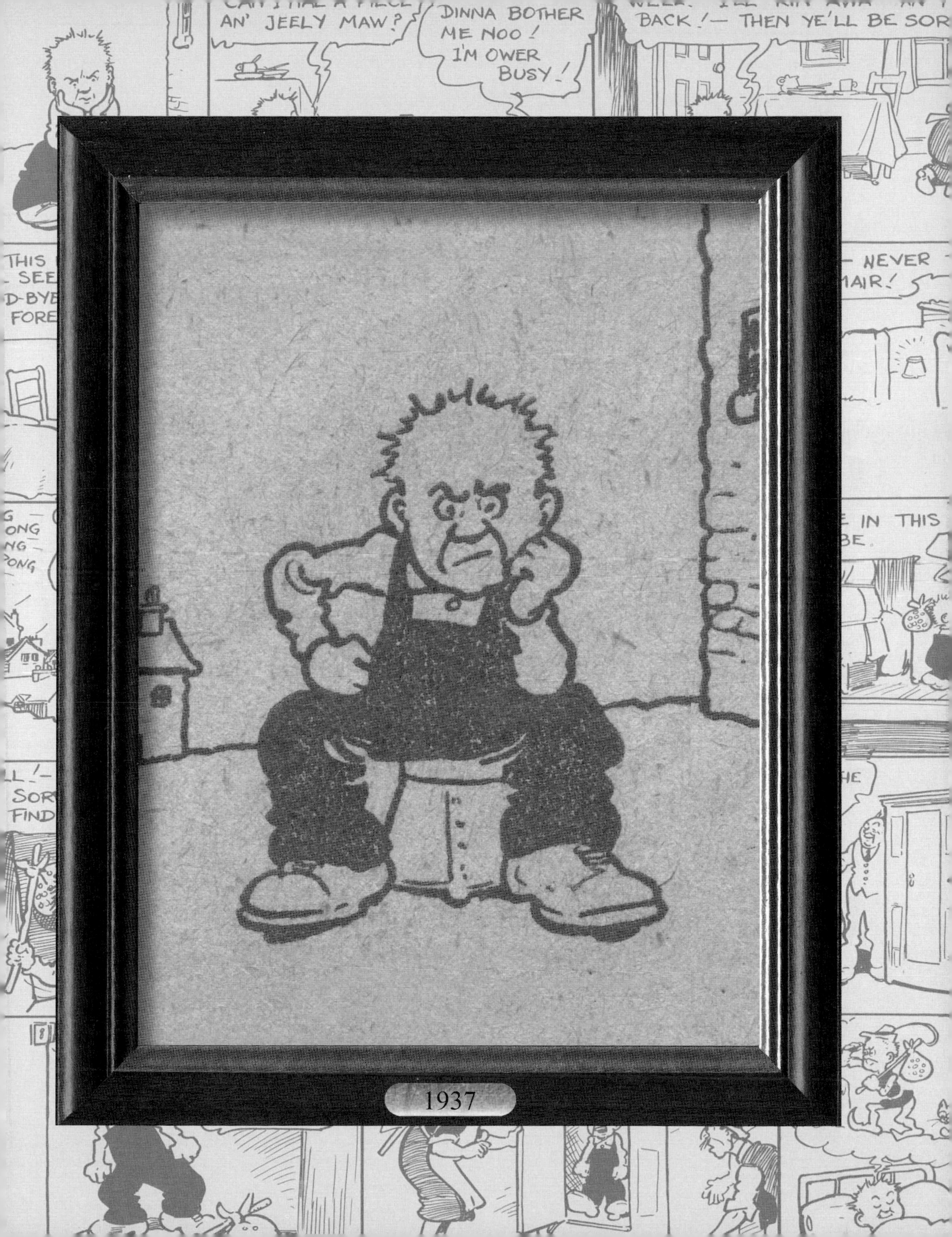

1937

THERE WAS AYE A GUID CROWD AT HAMPDEN IN THAE DAYS. . .

YOU DIDNAE GO ON THE INTERWEB TAE GET YOUR TICKETS IN THAE DAYS. YE QUEUED FOR HOURS
THE HAM
ON MATCH DAY THE CAR PARK WAS AYE FULL TAE THE GUNNELS, TAE. WISH I COULD AFFORD A MOTOR LIKE THAT.

BUT IT WAS WORTH IT TAE SEE THAE SCOTS LADS PLAY. GET AWA' INTAE THEM, LADS!
DEN
ROAR
THE BIGGEST NOISE O' THE LOT WAS FOR THE BROONS MEN WHEN MAW CHUCKED OOT THEIR SCOTLAND SCARVES AND BOCHT BONNIE PATTERNED ANES INSTEAD.
AH'M IN THERE. DO YE SEE ME? I'M THE ANE IN THE BUNNET!
. . .FOWK WERE JAMMED IN LIKE SARDINES TAE SEE A SCOTLAND GAME OR FOR THE CUP FINAL.

WELL, I'LL LEAVE THE VACUUM CLEANER FOR A FEW DAYS, I KNOW YOU'LL BUY IT WHEN YOU'VE TRIED IT MADAM!
I REALLY DINNA WANT IT,— BUT IT'S BRAW!
WULLIE! COME AN' GET YER PORRIDGE!
OCH! I DINNA LIKE PORRIDGE!
COME ON, EAT 'EM— YE'LL GROW A BIG LADDIE, WI' NICE CURLY TEETH AND WHITE HAIR!
UGH!
SUCK
S-S-L-L
WELL MADAM, HAVE YOU THOUGHT ABOUT IT?
NA! IT'S OWER DEAR!
LOOK HERE!— THERE ARE OTHER THINGS IT CAN DO. FOR INSTANCE, IF YOU REVERSE THIS TUBE IT ACTS AS A BLOWER
NOW, WATCH ME BLOW THE DUST OFF YOUR LITTLE BOYS OVERALLS!
PORRIDGE!!!

The Sunday Post 28th February 1937

OH! MRS BROON!— YER HOOSE HAS BEEN BROKEN INTO!— I SAW THE MAN GETTIN' IN THE KITCHEN WINDIE!
DINNA MAK A NOISE!—I'LL UNLOCK THE DOOR!
YOU GANG IN FIRST HEN!
NA! YOU FIRST!
LOOK AT PAW SHAKIN'!
HUH! WE'LL TEACH THAT BURGLAR!
YES! THERE'S BEEN A BURGLAR— THE HOOSE IS A' IN A MESS!— FETCH THE POLIS!
HE MUST BE ABOOT FIFTEEN FUT!
S'A RICHT MRS. BROON, I SEEN A MAN HANGIN' ROOND HERE TH' NICHT, I KEN WHAR HE BIDES,- I'LL GET HIM!!
WHIT A DINKY POLISMAN!
A GUID PLOOMAN WASTED!
WEEL! WE'VE LOOKED A' OWER THE HOOSE, BUT NAETHIN'S MISSIN', EXCEPT THE BURGLAR'S HAD A GUID FEED, MADE A FIRE, AN' SMOKED THE LAST O' PAW'S TABACCA!
THANK GUIDNESS MA BOOLS ARE SAFE!
RAT-TAT!!
THERE'S THE DOOR! MAYBE IT'S THE POLIS WI' THE BURGLAR!
AYE! IT'S ME! I WIS JUIST BACK FOR MA PIPE!— I LEFT IT HERE LAST NICHT!
WHY IT'S GRAN'PAW!
I'M ASHAMED O' YE!

The Sunday Post 6th June 1937

TOYS, GAMES
I COULDNA BUY ONY O' THEY TOYS,—MA WID SAY SHE COULDNA AFFORD IT!
DREAM
SNORE
TOYS
YOU CAN HAVE ANY OF THESE TOYS!
WHOOPEE!!!
I DIDNA KEN I COULD SKATE SAE WEEL!
GOAL!—HA-HA-HA!!
HI! YOU!— HERE'S SOME DOLLIES FOR YE!
MY HERO!
LUDO
TOYS
WULLIE'S SHed
WULLIES Hoose
SOAP
— IS THE CAR STILL THERE?

The Sunday Post 13th June 1937

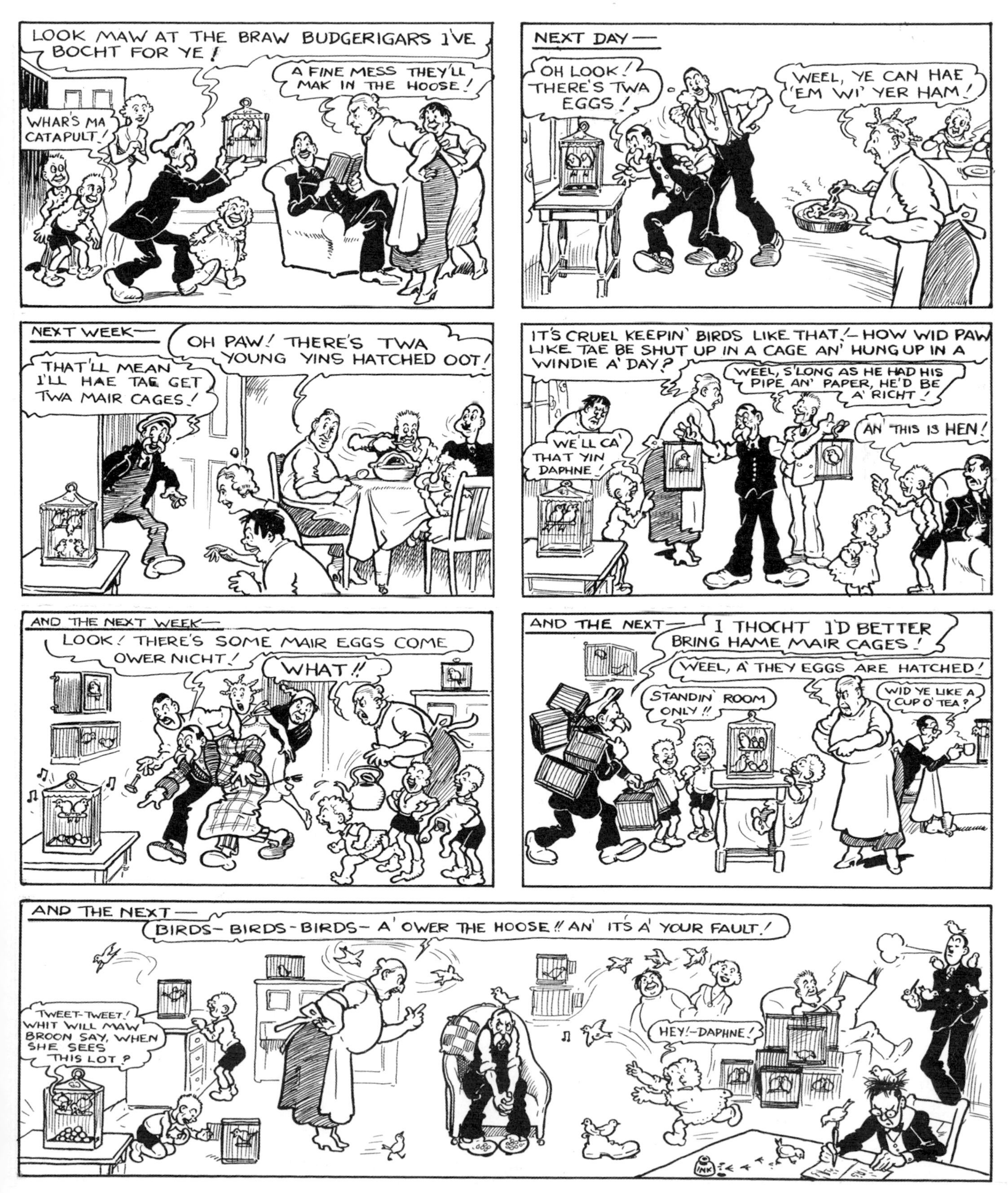
LOOK MAW AT THE BRAW BUDGERIGARS I'VE BOCHT FOR YE!
A FINE MESS THEY'LL MAK IN THE HOOSE!
WHAR'S MA CATAPULT!
NEXT DAY—
OH LOOK! THERE'S TWA EGGS!
WEEL, YE CAN HAE 'EM WI' YER HAM!
NEXT WEEK—
OH PAW! THERE'S TWA YOUNG YINS HATCHED OOT!
THAT'LL MEAN I'LL HAE TAE GET TWA MAIR CAGES!
IT'S CRUEL KEEPIN' BIRDS LIKE THAT!— HOW WID PAW LIKE TAE BE SHUT UP IN A CAGE AN' HUNG UP IN A WINDIE A' DAY?
WEEL, S'LONG AS HE HAD HIS PIPE AN' PAPER, HE'D BE A' RICHT!
AN' THIS IS HEN!
WE'LL CA' THAT YIN DAPHNE!
AND THE NEXT WEEK—
LOOK! THERE'S SOME MAIR EGGS COME OWER NICHT!
WHAT!!
AND THE NEXT—
I THOCHT I'D BETTER BRING HAME MAIR CAGES!
WEEL, A' THEY EGGS ARE HATCHED!
STANDIN' ROOM ONLY!!
WID YE LIKE A CUP O' TEA?
AND THE NEXT—
BIRDS- BIRDS- BIRDS- A' OWER THE HOOSE!! AN' IT'S A' YOUR FAULT!
TWEET-TWEET! WHIT WILL MAW BROON SAY, WHEN SHE SEES THIS LOT?
HEY!—DAPHNE!
INK

The Sunday Post 13th June 1937

WULLIE, YOU'RE TOP IN ARITHMETIC! I MUST REPORT TO THE HEAD-MASTER HOW WELL YOU'VE DONE!
WHILE I'M AWAY, YOU STAND HERE AND TELL ME IF ANYONE SPEAKS OR WASTES TIME.
IAN SOUTAR! – YOU SPOKE!
OH YEAH?
YOU TELL ON ME, AN' I'LL PUNCH YER NOSE!!
WELL, I WILL TELL ON YE! I'M NO SCARED O' YOU!
SLAP
REGISTER
S'A'RICHT WULLIE, WE'RE ON YOUR SIDE!
THANKS BOYS!
I'VE LEFT HIM IN CHARGE, TO KEEP THE CLASS IN ORDER
I MUST GO IN AND SEE THE BOY MYSELF.
CLASS 5
WELL! I'VE KEPT 'EM IN ORDER, MISS!

The Sunday Post 4th July 1937

THE MILKMAN SAID HE COULD GET ME A DUG FOR FIVE BOB! – WID YOU LIKE IT ?
AYE! WE WID! WE'RE NEEDIN' A HOOSE DUG!
WEEL, I'LL BRING YE THE DUG TH' MORN'S NICHT!
THANKS A MILLION BABY!
THANKS AWFY! GRAN'PAW
IT'LL BE RARE TAE HAE A DUG TAE WATCH THE HOOSE, WHEN WE GANG OOT, AN' AT NICHT!
WE'LL MAK A BRAW KENNEL FOR IT!
AYE!
LOOK! WILD DUG!
WHOOF WHOOF
I'LL PIT THIS IN THE BACK GREEN
I'VE BOCHT A MUZZLE IN CASE IT'S FIERCE!
BEWARE of the DUG!
I'M PLAYIN' AT HOOSES!
PAINT
LOOK! – I'VE GOT A BRAW DUG COLLAR!
AN' THIS IS THE BEST DUG LEASH THEY HAD IN THE SHOP!
WHARE'S THE BAIRN? IT'S TIME SHE WIS IN BED!
HE! HE!
RAT-TAT! KNOCK-KNOCK BANG!
THERE'S GRAN'PAW NOO! – WI' OOR DUG. BE CAREFUL IT DOESNA BITE YE!
I'M SCARED!
WEEL! – HERE'S THE DUG!!
HUH! A PEN WIPER!
OOR DUG!

The Sunday Post 15th August 1937

CAN I HAE A PIECE AN' JEELY MAW?
DINNA BOTHER ME NOO! I'M OWER BUSY!
WEEL!– I'LL RIN AWA AN' NO COME BACK!– THEN YE'LL BE SORRY!
THIS IS THE LAST TIME I'LL SEE MA WEE BED! GOOD-BYE!–I'M GAEIN' AWA TAE FOREIGN LANDS!
FAREWELL, SHED,– WE'VE BEEN GUID PALS,– MAW'S CROOL TAE ME,– I'M RUNNIN' AWA!
WULLIE'S ShED
THE AULD HOOSE!– NEVER TAE SEE YE ONY MAIR!
WULLIES HOOSE
DING DONG PING PONG
HARK!– THE BELLS!– THEY SOUND LIKE–"TURN AGIN WULLIE,– LORD PROVOST O' GLESCA!
–BUT THAT'S JUIST A LOT O' HOOEY, I'LL GET AWA IN THIS LORRY!
BAR
I'LL HIDE IN THIS WARDROBE.
BAR
WELL!– WE'RE AFF!– MA'LL BE SORRY WHEN SHE FINDS I'M GONE!
THIS IS THE HOOSE BILL,– FOR THE WARDROBE.
MAYBE I'M IN ENGLAND
OH AYE! THAT'S THE ONE I ORDERED BRING IT IN!
THEY'RE GOIN' TAE OPEN THE WARDROBE DOOR,– BUT I'LL NOT BE SENT BACK!
MICHTY!– HOW DID YOU GET IN THERE? COME ON,– AFF TAE BED WI' YE! IT'S GETTIN' LATE.
GLASGOW 5

The Sunday Post 5th September 1937

I SEE THE MACTAVISHES ARE GAEIN' ABOOT FLAUNTIN' THEIR NEW TARTAN SCARVES AN'A' THING —WHY CAN WE NO WEAR OOR TARTAN?
HERE'S A BOOK OF TARTAN, I JUIST GOT FROM THE LIBRARY! MAYBE OORS IS IN!
HEY! THEY'RE MA BOOLS!
OCH! THIS IS A ROTTEN BOOK!—THE BROON TARTAN'S NO IN!
HULLO FOLKS!
I DINNA THINK THERE EVER WIS A BROON TARTAN!
THE BROON TARTAN?—NA, THERE ISNA ANE! BUT MA GREAT GRAN'FAITHER'S UNCLE WIS A MAC SPEUG. I USED TAE WEAR THE TARTAN. I HAVE SOME YET, SO COME UP AN' I'LL SELL IT TAE YE!
AT GRAN'PAW'S
HERE YE ARE, SCARVES, TIES AN KILTS! THE LOT FOR A POUND!
RIGHT!
LOOK AT THEM!—I SOLD THEM THAT AULD STUFF FOR A QUID!
SAY SCOTTIES! I SURE LIKE YOUR TARTAN TRAPPINGS! I'LL BUY THEM ALL FROM YOU!— SAY THREE QUID!
O.K. BUDDY! —FOUR QUID!
FOUR QUID!
WHIT A MUG!

The Sunday Post 26th September 1937

GRAN'MAW'S COMIN' TAE STAY WI' US, SO YE MUST BE A VERY GUID LADDIE AN' DAE A' THING SHE TELLS YE!
NEXT DAY
WHIT A BIG LADDIE YE'RE GETTIN' WULLIE HERE'S A WEE PRESENT FOR YE!
THANKS GRAN'MAW!
I'M GAEIN' TAE BUY YE A NEW SUIT FOR YER BIRTHDAY! COME AWA NOO, AN' BRING YER WEE HORSE!
HEY! LOOK WHIT'S COMIN'!
SHAME
BOYS' SUITS
BOYS' OUTFI
NA! I DINNA LIKE THAT YIN!
I'LL TAK THIS YIN, HE CAN KEEP IT ON GAEIN' HAME!
WULLIE, COME BACK!
NOW THEN! WHIT'S GAEIN' ON HERE?
GRANMAW
LEN SLOSHEM

The Sunday Post 3rd October 1937

WEEL, WE'RE AWA TAE THE PICTERS, — SEE THAT THE BAIRNS GET TAE BED EARLY, MAGGIE.
WHIT ABOOT US HAEIN' A HALLOWE'EN PAIRTY? AN' PIT NUTS IN THE FIRE AN' A' THING!
THE NUTS ARE JUMPIN'!
I'LL GET MARRIED FIRST! MY CHESTNUT JUMPED BEFORE YOURS!
WHIT A LIE! MINE WIS OOT FIRST.
THAT'S THE MIRROR READY FOR DAPHNE!
HAUD THE CAN'LE UP TAE THE MIRROR DAPHNE, AN' YE'LL SEE YER LOVER!
!
WE'VE GOT SOME APPLES!
COME ON AN' GET YOUR SHARE O' THE CHAPPIT TATTIES!
BISCUITS
HELP! I'M FALLIN'!
HAE YE EVER TRIED SPEARIN' THE APPLES WI' A FORK LIKE THIS DAPHNE?
YE CAN DAE IT WI' A HATCHET TOO!
WHIT'RE YE DAEIN' DROPPIN' A' THEY HATCHETS AN' SAWS INTO MA GUID BATH?— AN' THERE'S WATER A' OWER THE FLAIR!
A' THE WATER'S RUN OOT THE BOTTOM MAGGIE!
PING
NAE WONDER THERE'S WATER A' OWER THE FLAIR!—DROPPIN' THEY HATCHETS AN' KNIVES IN, YE'VE MADE MA BATH LIKE A SIEVE!!

The Sunday Post 31st October 1937

OOH MAW! ARE YE MAKIN' THEY JELLIES FOR ME?
WEEL IF YE DAE YER HOUR'S PIANO PRACTICE MAYBE YE'LL GET A WHOLE JELLY TAE YERSEL'!
OCH! GIE ME IT WI'OOT PRACTISIN'.
NA-NA!—YOU PRACTISE FOR AN HOUR—WI'OOT STOPPIN'!
GET ON WI' THAT PIANO PRACTICE!
THIS IS AWFY! —HULLO! HERE'S JOCK AN' PIANIST PERCY!
HEY PERCY!—I BET YE COULDNA PLAY MY DIFFICULT MUSIC FOR AN HOUR ON OOR PIANO—IT WID GET YE DOON!
HA-HA-HA! I CAN PLAY ANYTHING—AN' FOR HOURS AN' HOURS!
WEEL COME IN AN' PROVE IT!
LISTEN! I'LL SHOW YE I CAN PLAY YOUR EASY MUSIC FOR AN HOUR!
WE'LL HAE A GAME O' SNAKES AN' LADDERS!
I BET YE CAN'T PLAY MA SCALES THOUGH!
OH YEAH?
MY! WULLIE'S PLAYIN' AWFY WEEL, AN' HE'S BEEN AT IT NEARLY AN HOUR TOO!
I WONDER IF IT IS THAT WEE WRETCH THAT'S PLAYIN'—IT'S OWER GUID!
JUIST AS I THOCHT! OH HULLO PERCY. IT'S NICE OF YOU TO COME AN' PLAY TO US. WULLIE NEVER DOES HIS PIANO PRACTISING!
OCH, THAT'S A' RICHT. WULLIE BET ME I COULDN'T PLAY HIS MUSIC FOR AN HOUR!
!
WAIT A MINUTE I'VE GOT A SURPRISE FOR YE!
S'FUNNY!—MAW'S NO MAD AT ME!
THERE'S A NICE JELLY FOR YE—TUCK IN!
OH NO, YE DINNA GET ONY! YE DIDNA PRACTISE YER MUSIC—SO YE CAN STAND OWER THERE AN' WATCH PERCY EAT ALL YOUR JELLY!

The Sunday Post 21st November 1937

NOO THAT THEY'RE A'OOT, I CAN GET DOON AN' POLISH THE KITCHEN LINOLEUM.
POLISH
MERCY ME! THE ROADS ARE AWFY ICY! — MIND YE DINNA FA' AN' BRAK YER NECKS!
OH DEAR! I WANT TAE CROSS THE ROAD — AN' I'M FEARED! — IT'S SAE SLIPPERY!
DINNA WORRY GRAN'MAW, I'LL SEE YE SAFE ACROSS!
SLIP
IT'S A' RICHT LADDIE, JUIST HANG ON TAE ME!
OH GOSH! — I NEARLY FELL THEN, I'LL GET YE ACROSS THOUGH!
SKITE
THANKS FOR GETTIN' ME ACROSS LADDIE!
AYE, BUT I'VE GOT TAE GET BACK AGAIN!
THANK GOODNESS WE'RE SAFE BACK HAME WITHOOT ONY NASTY FALLS ON THEY AWFY ROADS!
AYE, WHIT A RELIEF TAE BE ABLE TAE WALK WITHOOT SLIPPIN'!
BUMP
CLAP CLAP
POLISH

The Sunday Post 19th December 1937

THE DANDY
No 1 DEC. 4 1937
EVERY FRIDAY
2d
HI! HI!
ALL YOU YOUNG FOLK!
GREAT NEWS!
FREE TO YOU
JUMPING FROGS
Given with every copy of the
GREAT NEW COMIC
2d
THE DANDY COMIC
OUT ON FRIDAY 10TH DEC.
DESPERATE DAN
I WANT A HORSE! AND IT'S GOTTA BE TOUGH BECAUSE I'M DESPERATE DAN!
THE HORSE DEALER OF BAD MAN'S GULCH
THIS IS A REAL TOUGH HORSE MISTER
IT'D BETTER BE!
BAD MAN'S GULCH 1 MILE
BAD MAN'S GULCH ½ MILE
SELL ME A DUD HORSE WOULD YOU?
What will Desperate Dan do to the swindling horse-dealer? There's a big laugh and an amazing finish in the rest of this funny set of pictures. See the complete set in—
No 1 OF THE GREAT NEW COMIC
THE DANDY
OUT ON FRIDAY, DEC. 3RD
PRICE 2D
FREE TO EVERY READER WITH THE NEW COMIC
THE GREAT EXPRESS WHISTLER
THE DANDY COMIC
JUMPING FROGS
The Dandy is packed full of comi
and pict
Many of The Dandy great comics appe in brilliant colours
Another Treat for You!
A GREAT SLAB OF TASTY
TOFFEE
THE DANDY TASTY TOFFEE
A REAL CREAMY CHEW THAT WILL MAKE YOUR MOUTH WATER
FREE
GIVEN ONLY IN
THE DANDY COMIC
On Sale Friday, February 18
Price 2d.
IN 1937, A NEW COMIC FOR CHILDREN WAS PUBLISHED. THE COMIC'S NAME WAS THE DANDY AND ADVERTS FOR THIS NEW PAPER RAN IN THE FUN SECTION ALONGSIDE THE BROONS AND OOR WULLIE, WHOSE ARTIST, DUDLEY D WATKINS, WOULD DRAW DESPERATE DAN STRIPS FOR THE DANDY FROM 1937 THROUGH TILL HIS DEATH IN 1969.

Copies of Issue 1 of the Dandy have sold for over £4000 at auction. Paw Broon is currently rummaging through cupboards in the hope of finding a copy.

A HAPPY NEW YEAR MRS SCOTT! —I'VE COME TAE FIRST FOOT YE!
OCH! YE CANNA COME IN, WULLIE! —YE'RE FAIR-HAIRED AN' IT'S NO LUCKY TAE BE FIRST FOOTED BY A FAIR-HAIRED LADDIE!
HA-HA! YE CANNA GET ONY POKES! I'M DARK-HAIRED AN' FOLKS LET ME FIRST FOOT THEM!
IT'S A SAIR FECHT!

1938

Wullie's Library

Wullie's a Sunday Post man through and through but he's always had an eye for a good read.

MICHTY. THESE BOOKS FAE THE 30s AN' 40s ARE PACKED FU' WI' BRAW STORIES O' COWBOYS AN' MOUNTIES AN A'THING. YE HAD TO WORK FOR YOUR STORIES BACK THEN, THOUGH. THERE WAS AYE PLENTY O' READING IN THAE DAYS. EVEN THE COMICS WERE MAIR WORDS THAN PICTERS.

THE BEANO COMIC
No 1 · JULY 30 · 1938 EVERY TUESDAY 2d
SOMEONE'S TAKEN MY EGG AGAIN
DID YOU TAKE MY EGGS?
NO! BUT I SAW ONE BY THE RIVER!
BIG EGGO
HE'S GOT MY EGG!
?
25 STAR STORIES FOR BOYS
Including "THE BLACK CRUSADER"
No 1 DEC 4 1937 EVERY FRIDAY 2d
COMIC
THE CAT
THE COWBOY BOOK for BOYS
"THE REBEL SWOT" — HIS AMAZING EXPLOITS START INSIDE
THE HOTSPUR
No 132 – MARCH 7 · 1936 – EVERY FRIDAY – 2d
LAND
EVERY BOY'S ANNUAL
THE MOUNTIES' BOOK
R.C.M.P. QUICK-FIRE ADVENTURE STORIES for BOYS
ROYAL CANADIAN MOUNTED POLICE

OOR WULLIE 1936-1946

A HAPPY NEW YEAR MRS SCOTT! —I'VE COME TAE FIRST FOOT YE!
OCH! YE CANNA COME IN, WULLIE!—YE'RE FAIR-HAIRED AN' IT'S NO LUCKY TAE BE FIRST FOOTED BY A FAIR-HAIRED LADDIE!
HA-HA! YE CANNA GET ONY POKES! I'M DARK-HAIRED AN' FOLKS LET ME FIRST FOOT THEM!
I'LL WEAR PAW'S CAP—THEN THEY'LL NO SEE MA HAIR!
SO YE WANT TAE FIRST FOOT ME? WEEL, LET ME SEE THE COLOUR O' YER HAIR!
NA! YE CANNA CROSS MA DOORSTEP! YE'RE NO DARK!
I'LL PIT THIS BOOT POLISH ON MA HAIR, THEN SOMEBODY WILL LET ME IN AN' GIE ME MA NEW YEAR!
OCH! YE CANNA KID ME, WULLIE!—I KEN YER HAIR'S NO DARK—AWA WI' YE!
GOSH! WHIT A LOT O' POKES YOU'VE GOT!
HA-HA! AN' I DIDNA HAE TAE BLACKEN MA HAIR TAE GET THEM EITHER!
HEY, JOCK! YOU'RE DARK. WILL YE LET ME FIRST FOOT AHENT YE?
AYE!
I'LL WALK IN RICHT AHENT YE—THE WIFIE'LL NEVER SEE ME COMIN' IN!
AWA YE GO THE BAITH O' YE, I DINNA WANT SOOT A' OWER MA CLEAN FLAIR—AN' WULLIE'S FAIR-HAIRED ONYWEY!
GOODBYE, MRS STEWART, AN' THANKS FOR THE POKE.
HULLO, GEORDIE, WHIT ABOOT YOU COMIN' TAE FIRST FOOT ME IN MA SHED AN' I'LL GIE YE SOMETHIN'!
OH! WID YE, WULLIE?
FANCY! YE'RE MA FIRST FOOT.
A HAPPY NEW YEAR GEORDIE, AN' NOO I'M GIEIN' YE AN AULD PIECE O' CHEESE OOT'N THE MOOSE TRAP.
WHIT?
—AN' THANKS VERY MUCH FOR YER FIRST FOOT PRESENTS—A' THESE POKIES! —GET OOT O' HERE!!

The Sunday Post 2nd January 1938

NA! YE'RE NO TAE GET ONY O' THIS DUMPLIN' TH' NICHT IT'S FOR THE MORN'S DINNER. AN' I'M LOCKIN' THE PRESS – THERE'S BEEN OWER MONY THINGS TA'EN OOT O' THE PRESS LATELY!
SNIFF
SNIFF
QUITE RIGHT TOO, MAW!
YE SHOULDNA LEAVE THE KEY O' THE PRESS LYIN' ABOOT MAW. SEE! I'LL PIT IT UNDER MA PILLOW FOR SAFETY. NAEBIDY'LL GET IT WHEN I'M SLEEPIN' ON IT!
I'M AWFU' HUNGRY HORACE. COME ON AN' LET'S BRAK INTO THE PRESS!
O.K. KID!
LOOK! I'VE GOT A BITTIE WIRE – WE COULD PICK THE LOCK O' THE PRESS DOOR – COME ON!
YE KEN, READIN' IN BED GIES YE AN' APPETITE! WHIT ABOOT US TAKIN' JUIST A WEE BITTIE O' YON DUMPLIN'?
I'LL GIT A SCREW DRIVER AN' SEE IF WE CAN GET THE DOOR OPEN!
I'VE BEEN STARVIN' EVER SINCE MAW MADE THE DUMPLIN'
WE'LL SEE IF WE CAN GET A KEY TAE FIT THE LOCK!
AW JINGS! WHIT ARE YOU TWA DAEIN' AT THE PRESS? YE'RE NO' AFTER THAT DUMPLIN' ARE YE?
MICHTY ME! THE HALE FAMILY'S COMIN'!
HULLO! WHIT ARE YOU KIDS DAEIN' IN HERE AT THIS TIME O' NICHT? AFF TAE BED WI' YE!
GOSH! THEY'RE A' AFTER THE DUMPLIN'
HOW TO PICK A LOCK
AYE!
AWA YE GO! WE'RE ON IMPORTANT BUSINESS.
IF YE WANT TAE OPEN THE PRESS, IT'S A SCREW DRIVER YE NEED. THIS'LL DAE IT!
NA! TRY A BITTIE WIRE!
JINGS! HERE'S MAW!
SO! – I'VE CAUGHT YE A' IN THE ACT! WHA STOLE THE KEY?
JINGS! THE DOOR'S BEEN UNLOCKED A' THE TIME!
MICHTY ME! LOOK AT THAT!!
?!?
IT'S GONE!

The Sunday Post 6th February 1938

OH WULLIE, HERE ARE YER COUSINS SHEILA AN' ETHEL. THEY'VE COME TAE STAY WI' US FOR A FEW DAYS!
NOO YE MUST TAK THEM BAITH OOT, AN' SHOW THEM ROOND THE TOON!
OH, HOW JOLLY!
SHAME
TAKE DOLLY FOR A WALK TOO!
JINGS!
HI! LOOK, WULLIE'S TURNED CISSY!
HULLO! NURSIE!
OH WHAT LOVELY DOLLS IN THIS SHOP!
WHIT BONNY CURLS YE'VE GOT, WULLIE!
LOOK! WULLIE YER HAIR RIBBON'S COME UNDONE!
TOYS
I'M GETTING TIRED PUSHING DOLLY'S PRAM. YOU PUSH IT FOR ME, WULLIE!
ME?
AND PUT MY GOLLY IN IT TOO!
MISERY
COME INTO MY SHED, QUICK!
DO YOU KEEP YOUR DOLLIES IN THERE?
NOO LISTEN!— I'M FED UP WI' YOU TWA! A' MA PALS ARE LAUGHIN' AT ME GAEIN' OOT WI' YE!
I'M ASHAMED O' YE AN' SICK TAE DEATH O' YER DOLLIES AN' YER PRAM!
—THAT'S FOR KICKING OUR DOLLIE'S PRAM!
WHAM
HAVE YOU HAD ENOUGH?
BRIGHT IDEA
SAY!—YE SHOULD HEAR WHIT MA PALS SAY ABOOT YOU TWA BEIN' A COUPLE O' STUCK-UP TOFFS! —THEY'RE OOT IN THE STREET NOO!
OH! IS THAT SO?
BONK

The Sunday Post 9th January 1938

PAW, TAK THE BAIRNS OOT TILL I'M READY. AN' DINNA LET THEM DIRTY THEMSELVES. I'LL BE READY IN HALF AN HOUR AN' MEET YE AT THE PARK GATES, THEN WE'LL A' GANG TAE MRS FARQUAHAR'S FOR TEA! MIND NOO, ONY O' YOU KIDS THAT GETS DIRTY'LL BE SENT HAME!
SOAP
POLISH
GLITTER
COME ON NOO, MIND WHIT YER MAW SAID. DINNA DAE ONYTHING THAT'LL MAK YE DIRTY!—JUIST BEHAVE YERSEL'S FOR ONCE.
SHINE
IF DIRTY NO—
IF DIRTY NO—
IF DIRTY NO—
IF DIRTY NO—
SQUEAK
GOSH! I'D LIKE TAE KNOCK THAT BOTTLE AFF O' THAT WALL- BUT I'D JUIST DIRTY MA HANDS!
I COULD DAE WI' SOME SWEETIES. BUT I'D GET A' MESSED UP!
CAN I NO' JUIST KICK THIS TIN ABOOT?
NA, YE'LL DIRTY YER SHOES THEN YE'LL NO' GET TAE THE PAIRTY.
SAY, WHIT ABOOT US GAEIN' OOT IN THIS AULD BOAT TILL MAW COMES?
OOH, GOSH! NO! WHY, WE'D GET OOR CLAES A' MUCKED UP ON THEY DIRTY SEATS.
TUT-TUT
NO! NO!
OCH! IT'LL BE A' RICHT! LOOK, I'VE PIT MA HANKY ON THE SEAT, I'LL NO' GET DIRTY NOO!
COME BACK PAW, THIS MINUTE!
AW! HELP!!- THE BOAT'S LEAKIN' —I'LL BE DROONED
MICHTY ME.!!
MA GOODNESS! YE'RE A NICE ANE TAE TAK CARE O' THE BAIRNS.—GETTIN' IN A MESS LIKE THIS YERSEL'!—TAK A HAUD O' MY GAMP, - I'LL PULL YE OOT!
SLIP
JINGS, LOOK! AFTER THEM TELLIN' US NO TAE GET IN A MESS!

The Sunday Post 6th March 1938

LOOK, I'VE FOUND A DUG. D'YE KEN WHOSE IT IS?
NA! I'VE NEVER SEEN IT BEFORE.
NOW I'VE LOCKED THE DUG IN MA SHED, I'LL GANG TAE THE POLICE TAE SEE IF THERE'S A REWARD FOR IT.
WHOOF
WHOOF
CLICK
OH WULLIE! I'VE LOST MA POMERANIAN -I'LL GIE YE SIXPENCE IF YE CAN FIND IT FOR ME.
O.K. MISS SMITH, I'LL FIND IT FOR YE. I'M GOOD AT DETECTIVE WORK.
SAY! WHIT'S A POMERANIAN? IT'S A FLOWER ISN'T IT— SORT O' GERANIUM?
HA-HA! AYE, THAT'S IT!
HEY! WHIT'S THAT YOU'VE GOT IN THAT BOX? IS IT A POMERANIAN?
POP
GOT IT AT LAST!—HEY YOU, JOCK THAMSON! WHAUR DID YE GET THAT POMERANIAN?
WID YE LIKE TAE SMELL IT WULLIE? I GOT IT IN MA STOCKIN' LAST XMAS
SQUEEZE
I'VE GOT TAE FIND THAT POMERANIAN. IT BELONGS TAE MISS SMITH AN' I'M TAE GET A REWARD IF I FIND IT.
WHIT! A REWARD? —LISTEN, A POMERANIAN'S A DUG,—AN' THERE'S ANE OWER YON WALL!
HA-HA! WULLIE'S A RICHT MUG!— I'LL GET THE POMERANIAN OOT O' HIS SHED AN' GET THE REWARD MYSEL'.
J. GLASS DOG BREEDER
AW GOSH! —I'M STUCK!
RIP
WHAT ARE YOU DOING, CLIMBING MY WALL?
WEEL, YE SEE, MISTER, I'M LOOKIN' FOR A LOST POMERANIAN!
A POMERANIAN! WELL, THERE'S ONE OVER THERE. BUT I'VE HAD HIM SINCE HE WAS A PUP!
JINGS! IS THAT A POMERANIAN?
MICHTY ME! AN' TAE THINK THAT DUG I PIT IN MA SHED WIS A POMERANIAN A' THE TIME!
OH GOSH! THAT BULLY'S TRYIN' TAE GET AT THE DUG!— HE'S OWER BIG FOR ME TAE FECHT!
BOW
WOW
Wullies Hoose
GOSH! IT'S ESCAPED!
AH! THE DUG'S ESCAPED. I'LL JUIST NAB IT AN GET THE REWARD NOW!
KNOCK
WELL, I TELT YE I'D GET YER POMERANIAN, MISS SMITH!
OH! WULLIE HOO CAN I THANK YE— COME IN!
MAMMA
JUIST EAT UP THEY CAKES AN' TARTS AN' HERE'S SIXPENCE TAE YERSEL'
OOH-GEE! THANKS AWFY!

The Sunday Post 20th February 1938

WEEL, IT'S DECIDED TAE FORM THE BROONS' CYCLIN' CLUB! AN' WE'LL HAE OOR FIRST RUN TH' MORN!
JINGS! WHIT A LOT O' NONSENSE! YE COULDNA STAY ON A BIKE TAE THE END O' THE STREET, PAW!
NOO FOLKS, ARE YE A' READY?
HELP! LOOK WHA'S COMIN'!-GRAN'PAW, ON HIS AULD BONE-SHAKER!!
I'LL HAE A HAM AN' EGG TEA FOR YE WHEN YE GET BACK! AN' SEE YE TAK CARE O' PUIR AULD GRAN'PAW AN' THE BAIRN!!
DINNA FASH YERSEL' MAW! WE'LL TAK CARE O' THEM!
DINNA YOU TRY AN' STEER MAGGIE!
WEEL, WHIT HAE I GOT HANDLE-BARS FOR, THEN?
THERE'S AN AWFY STEEP HILL DOON THE OTHER SIDE, GRAN'PAW! YOU AN' THE BAIRN HAD BETTER WALK DOON! YE MICHT NO' BE ABLE TAE STOP AT THE BOTTOM!!
GOSH! WHIT A HILL! THE BIKE'S HARDLY MOVIN'!
AYE! AN' I'M FEARED THE BIKE RINS BACKWARDS, BUT I'VE GOT THE BRAKES ON!!
JINGS! I'VE LOST MA PEDALS!— I CANNA STOP!!
HELP! MAW!!
PIG SWILL
MICHTY ME!!!
ME AN' THE BAIRN'S A' RICHT MAW! THEY TOOK CARE OF US!!
SHAME

The Sunday Post 5th June 1938

JINGS! WHIT A BIG HOLE IN THAT LUM IT CANNA BE SAFE LEAVIN' IT LIKE THAT!
WELL BILL, THE CHIMNEY'S READY FOR TOMORROW!
OH MY!-HERE'S A GREAT THING,-AN' AULD RUSTY STEAM ROLLER!
GEE, I WISH I WIS A STEAM ROLLER DRIVER!
IT MUST BE RARE PULLIN' A' THESE HANDLES. MICHTY ME!-HERE'S ANE THAT'S MOVIN'.-THE ROLLER'S RINNIN' AWA!
OH DEAR! IT'S GOIN' STRAIGHT FOR THAT CHIMNEY WI' THE HOLE IN IT!
CRASH
JINGS! THE STEAM ROLLER'S BURIED!
WHIT WIS THAT AWFY NOISE JUIST NOO? IT SOUNDED LIKE A FACTORY CHIMNEY FALLIN'!
NOISE?- OOH, -ER-MAYBE IT WIS JUIST THUNDER!
OH GOSH! IF THEY FIND OOT I DID IT! I HOPE NAEBODY SAW ME.
NOW THEN, LOOK WHAUR YE'RE GOIN'!
JINGS!- A BOBBIE!!
DID YOU SEE HOW THAT CHIMNEY STACK FELL?
AYE-I PUSHED IT OWER MYSEL'!
HA HA
THE WEE RASCAL! -TRYIN' TAE BE FUNNY WI' ME.
FOUR O' CLOCK IN THE MORNIN', AN' NO' A WINK O' SLEEP. I BET THAT BOBBIE THINKS I HAD SOMETHING TAE DAE WI' THAT CHIMNEY FALLIN',-AN' OH DEAR! I'LL HAE TAE GANG TAE PRISON AN' BRAK STANES INSTEAD O' CHIMNEYS!
LISTEN MAW "THE CHIMNEY THAT WAS TO BE FELLED TO-DAY WIS KNOCKED DOON LAST NIGHT" HA-HA!
JINGS!
Z
DID YE READ IN THE PAPERS THIS MORNIN' ABOOT THE CHIMNEY BEIN' KNOCKED DOON? WELL-I DID IT-HA-HA!!
AWA' YE GO!
SURE! I KNOCKED THE LUM OWER MYSEL'
OCH AWA!
ARE YE TRYIN' TAE KID US YE'RE A TOUGH GUY WULLIE?
FANCY ME OWNIN' UP TAE A' BODY!- AN NAEBODY BELEIVIN' ME!!

The Sunday Post 27th February 1938

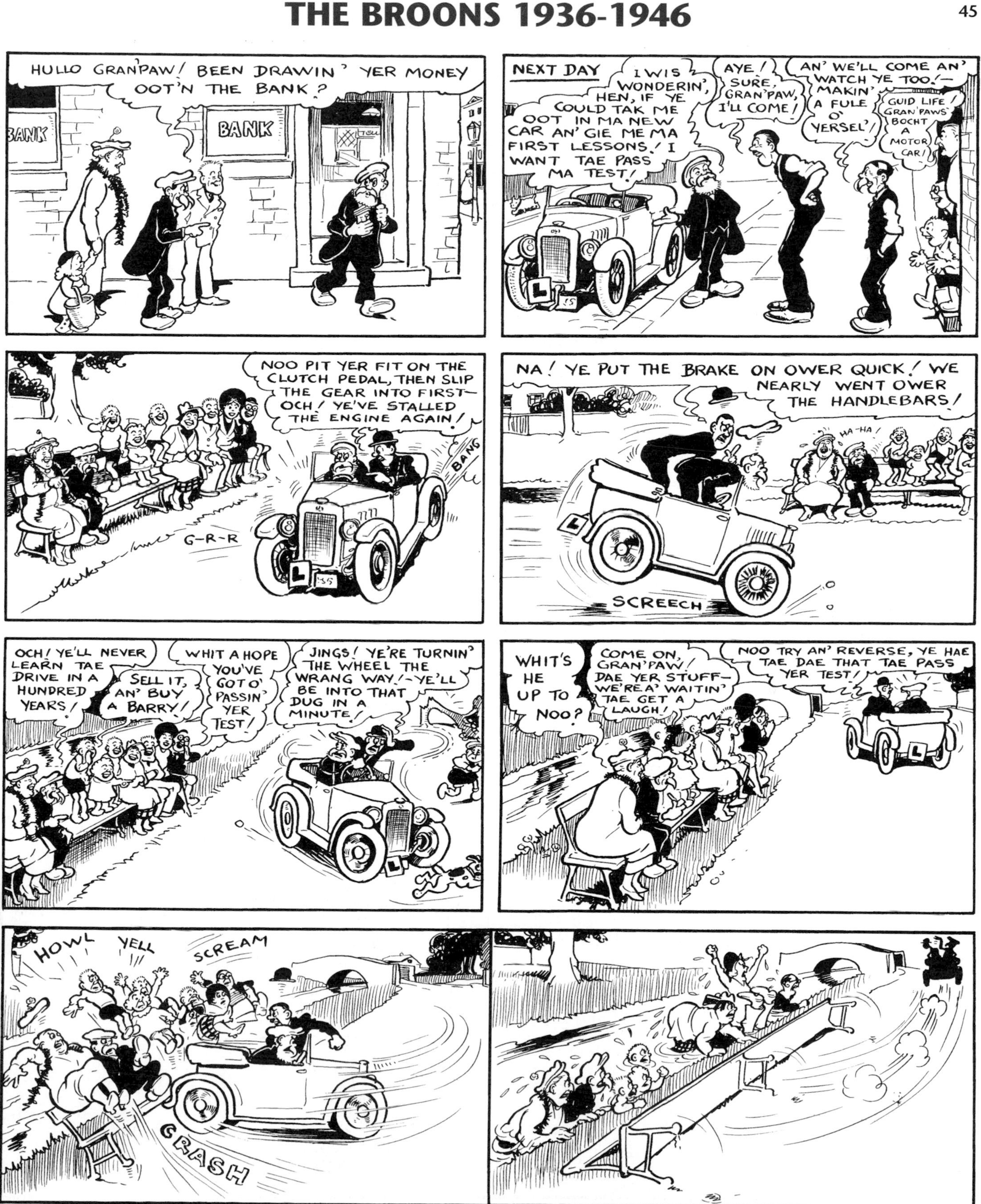
HULLO GRAN'PAW! BEEN DRAWIN' YER MONEY OOT'N THE BANK?
BANK
BANK
NEXT DAY
I WIS WONDERIN', HEN, IF YE COULD TAK ME OOT IN MA NEW CAR AN' GIE ME MA FIRST LESSONS! I WANT TAE PASS MA TEST!
AYE! SURE, GRAN'PAW, I'LL COME!
AN' WE'LL COME AN' WATCH YE TOO!— MAKIN' A FULE O' YERSEL'!
GUID LIFE! GRAN'PAWS' BOCHT A MOTOR CAR!
NOO PIT YER FIT ON THE CLUTCH PEDAL, THEN SLIP THE GEAR INTO FIRST— OCH! YE'VE STALLED THE ENGINE AGAIN!
BANG
G-R-R
NA! YE PUT THE BRAKE ON OWER QUICK! WE NEARLY WENT OWER THE HANDLEBARS!
HA-HA!
SCREECH
OCH! YE'LL NEVER LEARN TAE DRIVE IN A HUNDRED YEARS!
SELL IT, AN' BUY A BARRY!
WHIT A HOPE YOU'VE GOT O' PASSIN' YER TEST!
JINGS! YE'RE TURNIN' THE WHEEL THE WRANG WAY!—YE'LL BE INTO THAT DUG IN A MINUTE!
WHIT'S HE UP TO NOO?
COME ON, GRAN'PAW! DAE YER STUFF— WE'RE A' WAITIN' TAE GET A LAUGH!
NOO TRY AN' REVERSE, YE HAE TAE DAE THAT TAE PASS YER TEST!
HOWL YELL SCREAM
CRASH

The Sunday Post 19th June 1938

PHOTIES
GEE! LOOK AT THIS PHOTIE O' ERROL FLYNN! HE'S MY HERO!
I COULD GIE YE A PHOTIE O' ME, —JUIST AS HEROIC AS THAT!
I'LL LOOK IN THE AULD PHOTIE BOX, TAE SEE IF THERE'S ONY DECENT ANES O' ME!
WULLIE! HERE'S FAT BOB TAE SEE YE!
PHOTIES
I WANT TAE GIE WEE JEANNIE A SWANK PHOTIE O' ME, BUT A' THESE ARE GEY AULD FASHIONED!
OCH! THERE'S NAETHIN' HERE THAT'S GUID O' ME!
PHOTIE
PHOTIES
SAY, WULLIE! - I'LL TAK YER PHOTIE, I'VE GOT A CAMERA!
JINGS! WID YE BOB?
THANKS, BOB! I'LL HAE TAE THINK O' A GUID POSE!
I'LL RIN AN' GIT MA CAMERA!
A PHOTIE O' THIS'LL LOOK AS IF I'VE CLIMBED RICHT TAE THE TAP O' A HOOSE!
OW! - I'M SLIPPIN'!
SLIP
NEVER MIND, WULLIE, I GOT A RARE PICTER O' YE AFORE YE FELL!
WE'LL TRY ANOTHER ANE!
SQUELCH
ARE YE READY WULLIE?
AYE!
HO! SAE YE WANT TAE FECHT, EH?
HEY! -YE BIG BULLY!
-BUT DID YE GIT A PICTER?
I DINNA KEN, YE'LL HAE TAE TRY ANITHER POSE!
NOO MAK A GUID ANE THIS TIME, — DIVIN' INTO THE WATTER!
GEE! I'M FED UP O' THIS!
OCH, AYE! I'LL GET THE SPOOL DEVELOPED!
NEXT DAY
THERE'S ONLY AE PHOTIE! — BUT COME ON, I'LL SHOW IT YE WHEN WE SEE JEANNIE!
O.K. THEN.
HA-HA-HA
I PINCHED THAT FROM YER AULD PHOTIES, WULLIE!
WULLIE
WHIT ABOOT THEY ANES YE TOOK YESTERDAY?
HA-HA-HA! I DIDNA HAE A SPOOL IN MA CAMERA!

The Sunday Post 15th May 1938

PAW! THERE'S AN AWFY LEAK COMIN' FROM UNDER THE SINK SOMEWHERE, —LOOK AT IT! WE'LL HAE TAE GET THE PLUMBER!
NA-NA! YE DINNA NEED A PLUMBER! HUH! SANDY LOW'S A DAB HAND AT THIS KIND O' THING, AN' HE'S GOT SOME BRAW TOOLS! — ME AN' HIM'LL SORT IT IN NAE TIME!
LATER.
YE SEE, SANDY, IT'S NO' A DRIPPIN' TAP, THE WATTER'S COMIN' FROM THE PIPES SOMEWHERE!
WEEL, MAYBE ANE O' THE PIPES NEEDS SOLDERIN'!
I'VE TURNED AFF THE WATTER AN' THE GAS AT THE METER, PAW!
OCH AYE! IT'S HARD TAE KEN WHAUR THE WATTER'S LEAKIN', —RICHT ENOUGH!
WE'LL NEED TAE TAK SOME O' THEY PIPES AFF AN' SEE WHIT'S WRANG!
GIMME THAT CHISEL! — I SAW IT FIRST!
NA! MR LOW SAID I COULD PLAY WI' IT!
WHIT A WEE LEEAR!
HURRY UP, YOU TWA! — I WANT TAE GET MA DISHES WASHED!
WEEL! WE'VE GOT THE SINK AFF! AN' I'M GETTIN' A KIND O' MIXED UP WI' THE PIPES NOO!
WEEL, I THINK THESE TWA SHOULD BE JINED
TWO HOURS LATER
WEEL, THAT'S THAT! THE JOB'S DONE MAW! YE CAN GET YER DISHES WASHED, AN' NOO I'LL BILE SOME WATTER SO'S SANDY AN' ME CAN HAE A CUP O' TEA, SEEIN' IT'S EFTER CLOSIN' TIME!
TUT-TUT
JINGS! IT'S LIKE THE FOUNTAINS AT THE EXHIBITION!
GET OOT O' HERE AN' DINNA YOU DARE COME BACK TILL YE'VE GOT A PLUMBER — A RICHT MAN!

The Sunday Post 2nd October 1938

OOR WULLIE 1936-1946

FANCY! A HALE SHILLIN' TAE MASEL' — I WONDER WHIT I'LL BUY WI' IT?
I'LL GET "THE DANDY" AN' "THE BEANO" - THAT'S FOURPENCE, THEN EIGHTPENCE WORTH O' TOFFEE APPLES AN' SUGARELLY!
HULLO, TEACHER! I'VE GOT A SHILLIN' TAE SPEND A' TAE MASEL'
WHY! YOU SURELY WOULDN'T BE SO GREEDY WILLIAM! IT WOULD BE MUCH KINDER TO SPEND SOME OF IT ON A LITTLE PRESENT FOR YOUR MOTHER, FOR INSTANCE!
AYE! THAT'S RICHT ENOUGH-I OUGHT NOT TAE BE SELFISH! I'LL GO FIFTY-FIFTY WI' MAW, AN BUY HER A WEE PRESENT!
JINGS! I COULD DO FINE WI' A BOB'S WORTH O' SWEETIES A' TAE MASEL'— BUT NA! — I'LL BE UNSELFISH!
CONFECTIONER
I WONDER IF I COULD GET MAW A NEW PAIR O' SHOES FOR SIXPENCE!
AH! THE VERY THING! — MAW'S AWFY FOND O' BANANAS!
BANANAS
THAT'S TWELVE BANANAS I'VE BOCHT WI' MA SHILLIN'! SIX FOR MAW AN' SIX FOR ME!
OH BOY! THAT MAKS ME FEEL HUNGRY! AN' THEY BANANAS LOOK GOOD!
WEEL, I'LL JUIST HAE WAN O' MA AIN BANANAS — I DINNA WANT TAE DRAP DEID ON MA WAY HAME!
MAN! THAT WIS CHAMPION! I'LL HAE ANITHER ANE-JUIST ANE!!
HULLO WULLIE! LOOK AT MA NEW PEN-KNIFE,— IT'S A DINGER!
I'LL GIE YE A BANANA FOR IT!
NA! TWA BANANAS!
O.K., THEN!
I'LL EAT A COUPLE O' BANANAS MASEL' TAE KEEP YE COMPANY!
H-M! SIX LEFT! THAT'S THREE FOR MAW AND THREE FOR ME!
OCH! I THINK I'LL EAT TWA O' MA AIN — THEY'RE RIPE, AN' THEY MICHT GO BAD AFORE I GET HAME!
MAW'S SURE TAE MAK ME TAK ANE O' HERS,— SO I MICHT AS WEEL EAT IT NOO!
NOW THAT'S THREE LEFT FOR MAW— BUT JINGS! MAYBE SHE'S GONE RICHT AFF BANANAS!
LOOK MAW! I'VE BROCHT YE A PRESENT! AH KEN YE LIKE BANANAS!
OH, THANK YE, WULLIE! BUT I'VE JUIST HAD AN APPLE — EAT IT YOURSELF!
JINGS! THAT'S AWFY KIND O' YE, MAW!
COME ON WULLIE, I'VE GOT YOUR FAVOURITE FOR TEA — A BRIDIE!
OOH! I COULDNA EAT A THING!

The Sunday Post 9th October 1938

I'VE GOT AN AWFY DOSE O' THE CAULD, MAW!
AYE! YE'RE LOOKIN' REAL BAD. YE'LL NEED TAE GET TAE YER BED!
HEY! DINNA YOU CUT UP THE 'SUNDAY POST' CROSSWORD PUZZLE!
SNIP
YE SHOULD BATHE YER FEET IN A HOT MUSTARD BATH, AN' DRINK GRUEL, I'LL MAKE SOME!
PIT A SWEATY SOCK ROOND YER THROAT, PAW, AN' TAK A HOT LEMON DRINK!
I'LL TURN DOON THE BED!
NOW SUP YER GRUEL, PAW, WHILE IT'S HOT!
JINGS! WHA'S SOCK'S THIS I'VE GOT ON? I'M GETTIN' IT IN MA GRUEL!
I'VE GOT AN INHALER THAT'LL CLEAR YER HEID! YE BLAW IT UP YER NOSE!
NA! NA! HOT LEMON'S THE BEST, JOE!
COME ON, PAW! WE'LL WRAP YER CHEST WI' COTTON WOOL AN' YE'LL GET TAE BED WI' HOT WATER BOTTLES AT YER FEET AN' AT YER BACK!
OW!
YE'RE BURNIN' ME I'M SCALDED
NOO GET INTO BED, PAW, AN' KEEP WARM!
OH HULLO, GRAN'PAW! PAW'S GOT AN AWFY CAULD! WE'VE JUIST PUT HIM TAE BED!
OCH! THERE'S ONLY WAN SURE CURE! I'LL MAK TODDY FOR HIM!
NA! NA! TODDY'S NAE USE!
WEEL, IT'S BETTER'N HOT LEMONS!
A HOT BAG'S THE THING!
COME ON, PAW, TAK A SNIFF O' THIS!
NA! TAK SOME O' MINE, PAW, IT'S BETTER'N JOE'S!
PAW! GET OOT O' BED AN' HAE A HOT MUSTARD BATH!
LET'S TAK YER TEMPERATURE, PAW!
NA! NA! HE'D CATCH HIS DEATH!
FAIR WET
GET OOT O' HERE THE HALE LOT O' YE! I'D RAITHER BE HAUF DEID WI' THE CAULD THAN KILLED WI' KINDNESS!

The Sunday Post 18th December 1938

THON'S ENT
MAW SAYS SHIRLEY TEMPLE'S NO' AS BRAW A BAIRN AS ME!
THON FRED ASTAIRE AND GINGER ROGERS COULD FAIR CUT A RUG.
THE ROAD TO THE SINK? MY FAVOURITE DISHCLOOT? EVEN HOLLYWOOD FUNNYMAN BOB HOPE HID TO DAE HIS CHORES.
WHAUR THERE'S HOPE, THERE'S CROSBY. BING WIS TAP CROONER BACK THEN.
NBC
AND NOW, GRANPAW'S FAVOURITE JOK
WHIT'S THE DIFFERENCE BETWEEN BIN
CROSBY AND WALT DISNEY? WELL, BIN
SINGS BUT WALT DISNAE! AN' THAT JO
WAS AULD WHEN GRANPAW WAS A LADD

TAINMENT!
DOON AT THE YAIRD THEY SAY I DAE THE WORK O' TWA MEN - PITY IT'S ABBOTT AN' COSTELLO! THEY WERE A GUID LAUGH, THOUGH.
IT WOULD TAK' SHERLOCK HOLMES TAE WORK OOT WHIT US TWINS GET UP TO A' DAY.

OH DEAR! MA TYRES ARE FLAT AN' I'VE LOST MA PUMP! - I'LL GO TAE THE GARAGE AN' GET LARRY TAE BLAW THEM UP!
HULLO, SON! WHY AREN'T YOU RIDING YOUR BIKE?
MA TYRES ARE PUNCTUATED AN' I'VE COME TAE A FULL STOP!
HULLO, LARRY! COULD YE BLAW UP MA TYRES?
TWA GALLONS, MISTER!

1939

I AYE DAE MA EXERCISES EVERY NICHT! KEEPS ME FIT!
NEXT DAY
WHAT'S THAT YOU'VE GOT, JOE!
JOE AN' ME HAVE BOCHT THIS MUSCLE DEVELOPER. IT MAK'S YE STRONG AND KEEPS YE SPRY.
JINGS! HEN CANNA DAE IT!
AYE! YOU LOT CAN LAUGH, BUT THE BAITH O' YE COULD DAE WI' SOME O' THIS TAE GET YER FAT DOON!
HA! HA! WHIT A LOT O' NONSENSE!
S'A'RICHT MAW! THEY'RE A' SLEEPIN', NAEBODY'LL SEE US!
I HOPE THIS IS GOOD FOR SLIMMIN'!
NEXT DAY.
MAN, THAT'S GREAT! WHIT ABOOT ME HAEIN' A SHOTTIE?
NA! NA! YE'D NEVER DAE IT GRAN'PA! I WIDNA LIKE TAE SEE A PUIR AULD MAN STRAININ' HIMSEL'— YE NEED STRENGTH LIKE ME!
OOT O' MA ROAD!—I'LL SHOW YE! YE'LL NO TELL ME I'M NO STRONG!
CREAK
CRACK
SPLIT
STOP IT, GRAN'PAW! YE'RE PULLIN' THE HOOSE DOON!
CLONK
WHOOF
JINGS! LOOK AT THAT BUMP! WHIT A DINGER!
LOOK WHIT YE'VE DONE TAE MA GUID DOOR YE AULD TARZAN!

The Sunday Post 8th January 1939

JAN 1ST 1939
9 A.M.
SO THIS IS THE NEW YEAR, MAW.
YE'LL PIT ON YER SUNDAY CLAES AN GANG TAE YER AUNTIES AN' WISH THEM A' A HAPPY NEW YEAR!
I'LL BE BACK FUR MA DENNER, MAW!
HAPPY NEW YEAR AUNTY JESSIE!
HULLO WULLIE, COME AWA IN BYE AN GET YER NEW YEAR!
I'M NO LANG UP, WULLIE, THE HOOSE IS AYE IN A MESS EFTER HOGMANAY. EAT UP THAT SCOTCH BUN!
I'LL BE OWER TAE SEE YER MAW AT FOWER O'CLOCK.
TA! TA!
HAPPY NEW YEAR, MISTER! -TIME YE WIS HAME!
SAME TAE YOU!
AUNTY BELLA'S
KNOCK
I BET THAT'S WULLIE,- AN' ME WI'A CAULD- I SHOULDNA GET UP!
I BET AUNTY'LL BE GLAD TAE SEE ME!
WHIT A NUISANCE, GETTIN' A PUIR SICK BODY OOT O' HER BED!
I'M SORRY YE'RE NO WEEL, BUT JUIST STAY IN BED I'LL HELP MASEL TAE MA NEW YEAR! I LIKE BLACK BUN AN' SHORTIE!
AT UNCLE JOE'S
HULLO, WULLIE! WHIT'S THE MAITTER, IS THE HOOSE ON FIRE? IT'S ONLY TEN O'CLOCK!
NA! NA! HAPPY NEW YEAR TAE YOU!
JINGS! IT'S FREEZIN' CAULD, AN I HAVENA GOT THE FIRE ON YET!
WEEL, TA! TA! SEE YE WHEN YE COME OWER!
TONY ITALIANO
HAPPY NEW YEAR, TONY!
SAME-A TA YOU, WULLIE! HAVE-A DA RASPBERRA DRINK FOR YER NEW YEAR!
THENK YE!
YER DENNER'S READY, SON. STEAK PIE AN' TATTIES AN' DUMPLIN'!
HOORAY! MY FAVOURITES!
JINGS! THAT WIS A RARE DENNER- BUT I'M FEELIN' QUEER!
A HAPPY NEW YEAR
A HAPPY NEW YEAR
AW! BALONEY TAE YOU!

The Sunday Post 1st January 1939

SALE NOW ON
LOOK! THERE'S THE VERY STUFF FOR A SASH FOR MAGGIE'S NEW BLACK DRESS! IT WID ONLY COST ABOOT 1/11d
GENUINE REDUCTIONS
JINGS! THEY'RE STOPPIN' TAE LOOK AT THE SALES AGAIN!
AYE, WOMEN GANG A' ROOND THE TOON LOOKIN' IN SHOPS, THEN COME BACK TAE THE FIRST YIN!
WE'D BETTER WAIT IN THE SHOP A BIT, TILL MAW'S SPENT 1/11d, THOUGH IT'LL MEBBE TAK HER AN HOUR IN THE LANG RUN!
AYE, LET'S GET IN OOT'N THE RAIN!
IS THAT REAL, OR IS IT A DUMMY?
HEY!!
BUMP
AYE! IT'S A DUMMY RICHT ENOUGH!
WHAT CAN I DO FOR YOU, SIR?
THOUGHT NICE BIT O' STUFF!
IT SUITS PERFECTLY!
TRY THE RAINCOAT ON MY LITTLE BOY!
LITTLE BOY, HUH!
WHIT ARE YE DAEIN' ON MONDAY NICHT?
£4.19.6
PAW! LEND ME 8/11 FOR A BARGAIN BLOUSE I'VE GOT
THIS SCARF IS GOING FOR NEXT TAE NOTHING, PAW— JUIST 4/11½d—LEN' ME FIVE BOB!
SAY PAW! CAN YE LEN' ME 10/- FUR A NEW HAT I'M GETTIN' CHEAP!
I'VE JUIST GOT A REAL BARGAIN O' A RAINCOAT FOR HORACE, PAW— 19/11d PLEASE!
OH, PAW! I'M SHORT O' MONEY, LEND ME.....!
—AN' IT WIS ONLY TAE COST 1/11d.!!
JINGS! WHIT MADE YE BUY THAT TILE HAT?
WEEL, IT WIS A BARGAIN, AN' IT MICHT COME IN HANDY FOR A WADDIN'!
CRACKLE

The Sunday Post 5th February 1939

OOR WULLIE 1936-1946

COME ON, PADDY! JUMP THROUGH THIS,— I'M GAUN TAE TRAIN YE TAE DAE TRICKS!
!
OCH! YE DAFT GOAT!
HA! HA! WHIT A DOG!— IT'S NAE USE!
I'LL TRY AGAIN,— JUMP THROUGH IT PADDY!— NA! DINNA BITE IT!
HAW! HAW! HAW!
LOOK AT HIM CHEWIN' IT! TUT! TUT!— YE'RE NO' A SMART TRICK DOG BUT MAYBE YE'RE A GUID WATCH DOG!
I'LL DISGUISE MASEL' AN' SEE IF HE'S A GUID WATCH DOG!
Wullie's Shed
SCRATCH
G-R-R G-R-R
WHOOF
JINGS! MICHTY ME! HE'S A WATCHDOG A'RICHT! HEY, PADDY! CHUCK IT, YE'RE PULLIN' MA BREEKS AFF!
G-R-R
THROW DOON ANITHER PAIR O' BREEKS MAW!
COME INSIDE AT ONCE!
DROP IT, PADDY!
YE CAN JUIST WAIT TILL I MEND THEM!
—AN' DINNA YOU TEASE THAT DOG ONY MAIR!
YE'RE A GRAND WATCH DOG! I'LL TELL THAT ASS, FAT BOB, YE'RE A MARVEL! —WONDER WHERE HE IS!
HULLO! WHERE DID YE GET A' THEY LOLLIPOPS?
THEY WIS GIVIN' THEM AWAY AS SAMPLES AT THE NEW SWEETIE SHOP DOON THE ROAD!
HOO DID YE NO' TELL A FELLOW THEN?
WEEL, I CAME UP TAE TELL YE, BUT YER SILLY DOG WIDNA LET ME PAST THE GATE!!
?
HELP! HERE IT IS AGAIN!

The Sunday Post 8th January 1939

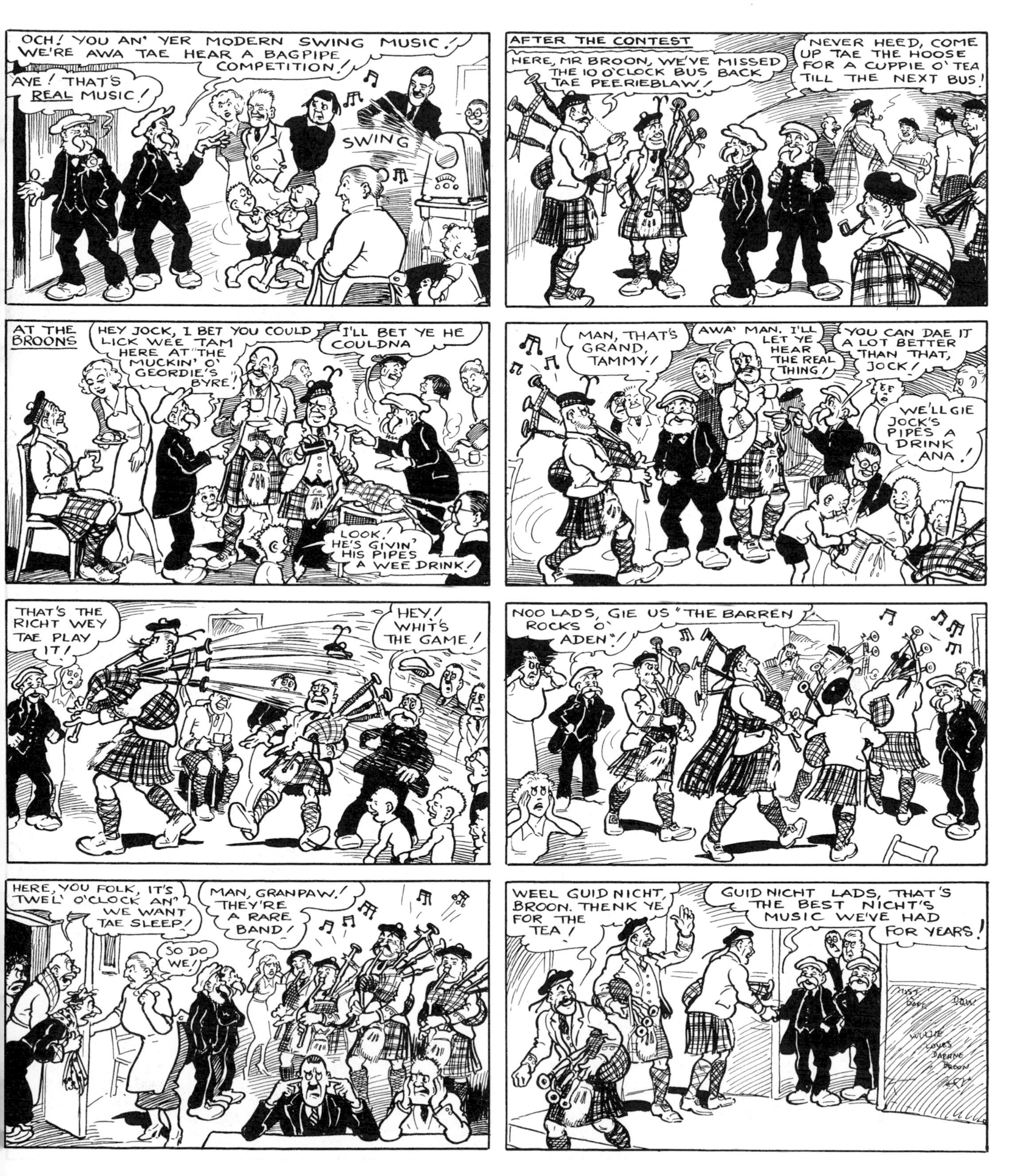
OCH! YOU AN' YER MODERN SWING MUSIC! WE'RE AWA TAE HEAR A BAGPIPE COMPETITION!
AYE! THAT'S REAL MUSIC!
SWING
AFTER THE CONTEST
HERE, MR BROON, WE'VE MISSED THE 10 O'CLOCK BUS BACK TAE PEERIEBLAW!
NEVER HEED, COME UP TAE THE HOOSE FOR A CUPPIE O' TEA TILL THE NEXT BUS!
AT THE BROONS
HEY JOCK, I BET YOU COULD LICK WEE TAM HERE AT "THE MUCKIN' O' GEORDIE'S BYRE"!
I'LL BET YE HE COULDNA
LOOK! HE'S GIVIN' HIS PIPES A WEE DRINK!
MAN, THAT'S GRAND, TAMMY!
AWA' MAN. I'LL LET YE HEAR THE REAL THING!
YOU CAN DAE IT A LOT BETTER THAN THAT, JOCK!
WE'LL GIE JOCK'S PIPES A DRINK ANA!
THAT'S THE RICHT WEY TAE PLAY IT!
HEY! WHIT'S THE GAME!
NOO LADS, GIE US "THE BARREN ROCKS O' ADEN"!
HERE, YOU FOLK, IT'S TWEL' O'CLOCK AN' WE WANT TAE SLEEP!
SO DO WE!
MAN, GRANPAW! THEY'RE A RARE BAND!
WEEL GUID NICHT, BROON. THENK YE FOR THE TEA!
GUID NICHT LADS, THAT'S THE BEST NICHT'S MUSIC WE'VE HAD FOR YEARS!

The Sunday Post 12th February 1939

OOR WULLIE 1936-1946

MAW, HERE'S THE TICKETS FOR THE CANTATA THE NICHT. THE PROVOST AN' A' THE NIBS ARE TAE BE THERE!
THAT NIGHT.
NOW, CHILDREN, ARE YOU ALL READY? BE SURE TO REMEMBER YOUR LINES.
HERE'S WHAUR WULLIE COMES IN, PAW. HE'S WAITIN' AHENT THAT DOOR FOR THE PAGE TO OPEN IT!
DANDY
HA! HA! HA!
RAIN—ER, I MEAN—HAIL, OH KING! I HEAR THE FOOTSTEPS OF APPROACHING TRAMPS!
OH DEAR! THAT SHOULD BE "THE TRAMP OF APPROACHING FOOTSTEPS," WULLIE!
BLUSH
HA! HA!
HA! HA! HA!
NOW, WULLIE, DON'T FORGET YOUR LINES AGAIN! DO IT AS WELL AS CECIL, HE IS VERY GOOD!
HUH! WULLIE'S NO USE!
I'LL SEE YER BOOTS OFF, YE MUTT!
NOW SAY YOUR WORDS TO ME BEFORE YOU GO IN!
BY MY HALIDOM, UNSHEATH THY SWORD SIR KNIGHT!
BY MY HALIBUT, PIT UP YER MITS AN' FECHT!—YE BIG LUMP O' SUET DUMPLIN'!
OW!!
TAKE THAT, YOU SCURVY VARLET!
OH!—YE WID, WID YE?
OOH!!
COME ON, I'LL WALLOP YE WI' FISTS!
GO IT! WULLIE!
CLOCK HIM IN THE SNITCH, WULLIE!
YOU BAD BOY! YOU SPOILT EVERYTHING! WHAT WILL THE PROVOST SAY?
OOH DEAR!!
AH! MR PROVOST!
LET ME CONGRATULATE YOU, MISS SNIFTER,—A VERY FINE CANTATA!
HERE, SON,—HALF A CROWN TAE YE!—BEST FECHT I'VE SEEN FOR YEARS!—AND I HATE CANTATAS!

The Sunday Post 12th March 1939

BREAKFAST TIME.
IT'S A GRAND DAY THE DAY, DAPHNE! WE'LL START OOR SPRING CLEANING!
AW JINGS! WHIT DAE YE NEED TAE SPRING CLEAN FOR!
WHAT! WOULD YOU LIVE IN A DIRTY HOUSE!
SUITS ME!
PAW'S
TEA-TIME
THERE'S YER TEA ON THE DRESSER—AN' DINNA BOTHER US, WE'RE THAT BUSY WE HAVENA A MEENIT!
I TELT YE THIS WID HAPPEN!
PIECE
JINGS! THIS IS NO' SYRUP IN THIS TIN, MAW,—IT'S FURNITURE POLISH, AN' I'VE SPREAD SOME ON MA BREAD!
HEY, DAPHNE! I DINNA MIND BREAD AN' JAM, BUT NO' BREAD AN' DUST! IT'S STICKIN' TAE MA PIECE!
THIS IS AWFY! FANCY SITTIN' WI' THE "TABLE" ABUNE YER HEID!
JAM
YE'RE JUIST A' IN THE ROAD! C'MON AN' HELP AN' WE'LL GET IT FINISHED IN NO TIME! HERE PAW! TAK THIS POLISH AN' RUB THE LEGS O' THAT CHAIR!
HERE'S A BRUSH FOR YE, JOE!
NO BLINKIN' FEAR!
I DINNA HOLD WI' SPRING-CLEANING ATA'! YE'RE NO ROLLIN' ME INTO IT!
WE'RE AWA TAE GRAN'PAW'S TAE GET PEACE AN' QUIET!
TRY AN' GET ME TAE BEAT A CARPET!—WHIT A HOPE!
WEEL, THAT'S A' WE'LL DAE THE NICHT! WHIT ABOOT GAEIN' OWER TAE GRAN'PAW'S AN' GET A CUPPY O' TEA?
AT GRANDPA'S
THEY JUIST CAM OWER WHEN I WIS THINKIN' O' STARTIN' MA SPRING CLEANIN'! THEY DIDNA SEEM VERY KEEN TAE HELP, BUT I WIDNA LET THEM REFUSE!
POLISH

The Sunday Post 16th April 1939

GOSH! HERE'S BATTLIN' JOE BUGGINS, THE BOXER FRAE THE CARNIVAL— HIYA, CHAMP!
CHAMP
I'M GONNA BE A BOXER LIKE YOU AE DAY, MR BUGGINS! HOO ABOOT A FEW TIPS?
WHIT? A WEE SHRIMP LIKE YOUSE? A'RICHT, COME ON WI' ME!
NOW, YOUSE HIT ME WI' YER LEFT, SEE?
A'RICHT, BUT I'LL NO' HIT YE OWER HARD!
THERE'S MA AUTOGRAPH FOR YOUSE!
SMACK
JINGS!
THERE'S ANITHER TIP FOR YOUSE— RICHT ON THE END O' THE NOSE!
STRETCH
STRETCH
OUCH!!
BOUNCE
MICHTY ME! WHIT'LL THE GAFFER SAY?
JINGS! I'VE LAID OOT MR BUGGINS! CRIVVENS! I'M THE CHAMP NOO!
GASP
GROANS
MEET THE CHAMP, LADS! I'VE JUIST LAID OOT JOE BUGGINS, THE CARNIVAL BOXER!
AWA YE GO!
WHA, YOU?
DINNA BE DAFT!
A'RICHT, IF YE'LL NO' BELIEVE ME, I'LL TAK' ON BAITH THE THREE O' YE— I MEAN, YOUSE!
THERE'S A LEFT FOR YOUSE!
AN' THERE'S MA AUTOGRAPH FOR YOUSE!
BATTLIN' WULLIE, THAT'S ME! I'LL KNOCK SPOTS AFF'N ONYBODY!
A'RICHT! THERE'S A YOUNG AUSTRALIAN AT THE CARNIVAL, I BET YE COULDNA GIE HIM HIS LICKS!
NAE BATHER AT A'!
A YOUNG AUSTRALIAN, EH? HUH! I'LL KNOCK HIM RICHT BACK TAE HIS GRANNY!
HE'S IN THERE, WULLIE!
I'LL NO' TAK' LANG— WAIT HERE! I'LL BE OOT IN A MEENIT!
BIFF
SCUD
HELP! MAW!
WALLOP
SEE THE BOXING KANGAROO
ALL THE WAY FROM AUSTRALIA— INSIDE
HA! HA! WULLIE, WE TELT YE IT WIS A YOUNG AUSTRALIAN—
AYE, BUT WE DIDNA TELL YE IT WIS A BOXIN' KANGAROO!!
I THINK I'LL GIE UP THE RING AN' TAK UP KNITTIN'!

The Sunday Post 13th August 1939

IN THE PARK
DAE YE MIND WHEN WE WIS COURTIN', MAW, HOO WE USED TAE WALK ALANG THIS PATH AN' SIT DOON AHENT THEY BUSHES!
BLUSH
OCH AWA! YE'RE GETTIN' SENTIMENTAL IN YER AULD AGE!
THIS IS THE AULD SEAT WE USED TAE SIT ON AN' HAUD HANDS. DAE YE MIND?
HEY! WE WERE HERE FIRST!
AWA! WE WIS HERE THIRTY YEARS BACK!
JINGS! WE CANNA EVEN SIT ON THE AULD SEAT A MINUTE,— AN' WHIT DID YE HAE TAE KEEK AT THAT COUPLE FOR, PAW? NAE WONDER HE WIS WILD!
AH WEEL, I WIS JUIST THINKIN' BACK TAE OOR AIN YOUNG DAYS. HERE, LET'S GO AN' SEE THE AULD RUSTIC BRIDGE WHAUR WE USED TAE STAND AN' WATCH THE DUCKS!
THANK GOODNESS THEY TWA AULD FOGIES ARE AWA!
AYE, IT'S BONNY! IT'S NO' CHANGED MUCKLE EITHER!
MICHTY ME! THERE'S ANITHER COURTIN' COUPLE!
HEY, MISTER! DAE YE NO' KEN TWA'S COMPANY AN' FOUR'S A PICNIC?
WE'LL HAE A LOOK AT THE AULD OAK TREE FOR AULD TIME'S SAKE,— YE MIND WE HAD A FECHT THERE WHEN WE WIS ENGAGED AN' I THREW THE RING ON THE GRUND, AN' YOU HAD TAE LICHT A HALE BOX O' MATCHES TAE TRY AN' FIND IT!
AYE, I MIND IT FINE! BUT WE NEEDNA BATHER GOIN' NEAR THE TREE! THERE'S ANITHER COUPLE THERE A'READY! WE'LL MAYBE GET SOME PEACE AT HAME!
AT HOME.
JINGS! YOU TWA ARE SHAIRLY NO' COMIN' IN HERE!
CRIVVENS! JINGS!— WE'D BETTER GO INTO THE KITCHEN!
AW, MAW!
IN THE KITCHEN
WE'LL PLAY AT HOOSES,— YOU'RE THE FAITHER, AN' I'M THE MAW!—
THE WASHIN' HOOSE IS THE ONLY PLACE LEFT FOR US TAE SIT IN PEACE!
NEVER MIND, PAW, WE WERE YOUNG OORSEL'S AINCE!
HEY! CAN YOU TWA NO' GET SOME OTHER PLACE TAE SIT?

The Sunday Post 28th May 1939

OOR WULLIE 1936-1946

GET OOT O' THIS! I'M PLAYIN' PIRATES AN' LOOKIN' FOR BURIED TREASURE!
YE'RE JUIST A BIG BULLY! I'LL GET EVEN WI' YOU YET!
HULLO, BILL! I WANT YE TAE DAE ME A FAVOUR—!
THANK YE, BILL!
WHIT A DROP THAT BIG MUTT'S GOIN' TAE GET!
AH! 'TIS THE WITCHING HOUR OF TWELVE! I WILL GO FORTH AND DO THE DARK DEED!
NOO I'VE BURIED IT, I'LL COVER IT UP AGAIN!
NEXT DAY
GOSH! WHIT A BIG STANE!
JINGS! WHIT'S THIS WRITIN' ON IT?— IT'S AWFY QUEER!
JINGS! THAT'S A GREAT FIND!— IT'LL BE WORTH A HUNDER POUNDS! YE SHOULD TAK IT TAE THE MUSEUM!
GOSH! IT'S CLOSED! WHIT'LL I DAE!
MUSEUM
WEEL, YE'LL GET THE HEAD MAN AT HIS HOOSE!
PANT
GASP!
GREAT! IT'S WONDERFUL! ANCIENT STONE WRITINGS! YOU'RE A CLEVER BOY! WAIT TILL I RING UP FOR PROFESSOR ALLAN!
I THINK IT'S LATIN!— IT'S CERTAINLY NOT GREEK—!
MAYBE IT'S SOME ANCIENT CODE FOR BURIED TREASURE— WE'LL HAVE TO LET THE B.A. SEE IT!
WEEL, I'LL NEED £20 FOR IT ONYWAY!
I THINK I CAN READ IT!
WHAT!!
TUT-TUT, BOY! DON'T BE IMPUDENT!
GOSH!— IT READS—"YOU ARE A LOT OF DAFT MUTTS—WULLIE"—BAH!!

The Sunday Post 3rd September 1939

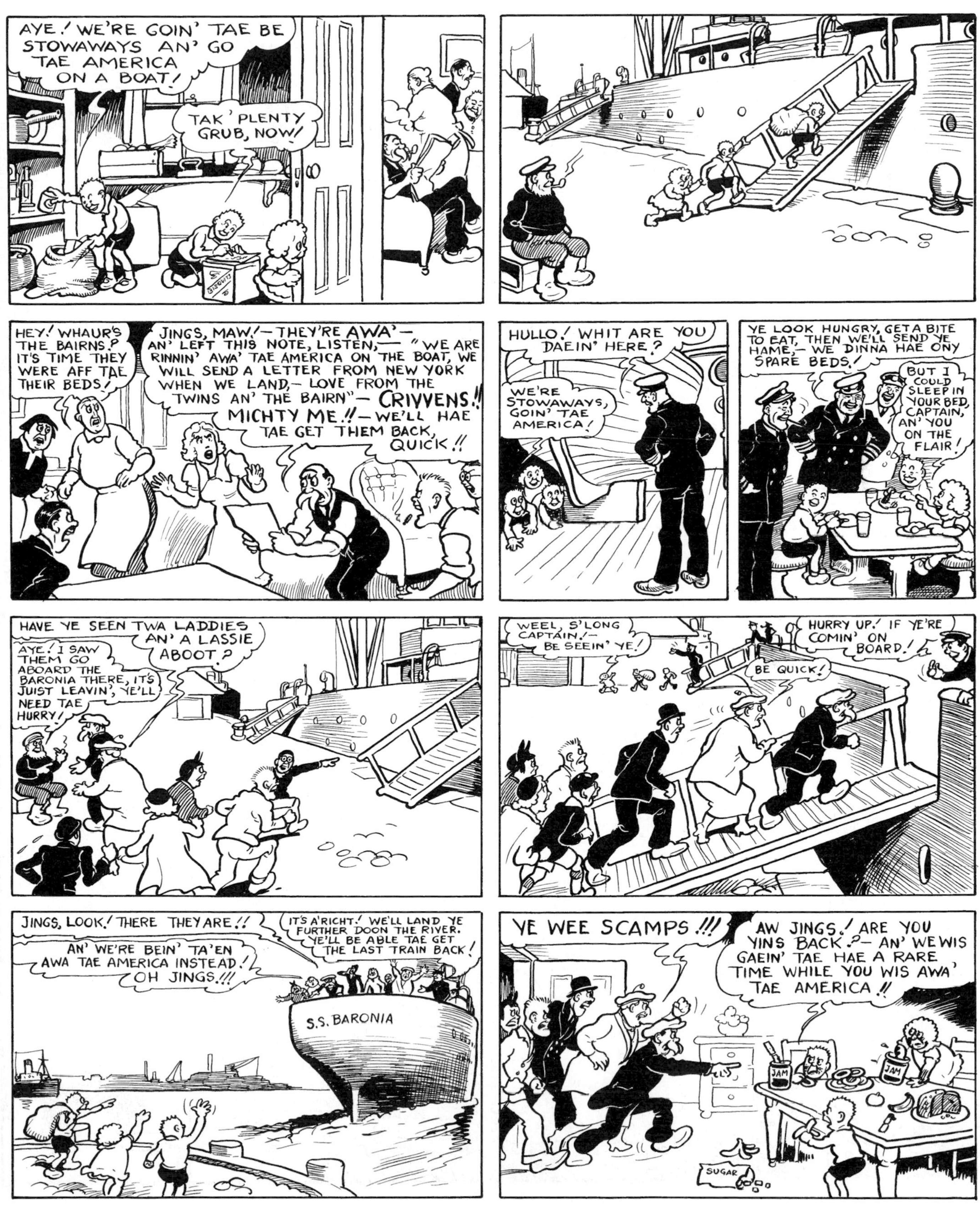
AYE! WE'RE GOIN' TAE BE STOWAWAYS AN' GO TAE AMERICA ON A BOAT!
TAK' PLENTY GRUB, NOW!
BISCUITS
HEY! WHAUR'S THE BAIRNS? IT'S TIME THEY WERE AFF TAE THEIR BEDS!
JINGS, MAW!— THEY'RE AWA'— AN' LEFT THIS NOTE, LISTEN,— "WE ARE RINNIN' AWA' TAE AMERICA ON THE BOAT, WE WILL SEND A LETTER FROM NEW YORK WHEN WE LAND,— LOVE FROM THE TWINS AN' THE BAIRN"— CRIVVENS!!
MICHTY ME!!— WE'LL HAE TAE GET THEM BACK, QUICK!!
HULLO! WHIT ARE YOU DAEIN' HERE?
WE'RE STOWAWAYS, GOIN' TAE AMERICA!
YE LOOK HUNGRY, GET A BITE TO EAT, THEN WE'LL SEND YE HAME,— WE DINNA HAE ONY SPARE BEDS!
BUT I COULD SLEEP IN YOUR BED, CAPTAIN, AN' YOU ON THE FLAIR!
HAVE YE SEEN TWA LADDIES AN' A LASSIE ABOOT?
AYE! I SAW THEM GO ABOARD THE BARONIA THERE, IT'S JUIST LEAVIN', YE'LL NEED TAE HURRY!
WEEL, S'LONG CAPTAIN!— BE SEEIN' YE!
HURRY UP! IF YE'RE COMIN' ON BOARD!
BE QUICK!
JINGS, LOOK! THERE THEY ARE!!
AN' WE'RE BEIN' TA'EN AWA TAE AMERICA INSTEAD! OH JINGS!!!
IT'S A'RICHT! WE'LL LAND YE FURTHER DOON THE RIVER. YE'LL BE ABLE TAE GET THE LAST TRAIN BACK!
S.S. BARONIA
YE WEE SCAMPS!!!
AW JINGS! ARE YOU YINS BACK?— AN' WE WIS GAEIN' TAE HAE A RARE TIME WHILE YOU WIS AWA' TAE AMERICA!!
JAM
JAM
SUGAR

The Sunday Post 25th June 1939

OH DEAR! MA TYRES ARE FLAT AN' I'VE LOST MA PUMP! - I'LL GO TAE THE GARAGE AN' GET LARRY TAE BLAW THEM UP!
HULLO, SON! WHY AREN'T YOU RIDING YOUR BIKE?
MA TYRES ARE PUNCTUATED AN' I'VE COME TAE A FULL STOP!
P
YJ 2474
HULLO, LARRY! COULD YE BLAW UP MA TYRES?
SURE, WULLIE!
AIR
THANKS! HOW MUCH IS THAT, LARRY?
THAT'S BUCKSHEE! IF YE WANT TAE KEN WHIT 'BUCKSHEE' IS, ASK YER FAITHER, HE'S AN OLD SOLDIER. HE'LL TELL YE!
WELL, I'LL HELP YE, FOR GIEIN ME A BLAW UP. WHIT'LL I DAE FIRST?
YE CAN HELP GINGER TAE OIL THIS CAR!
HERE, YE PUDDEN! THAT WIS MA EAR YE WIS OILIN'!
NOW, WULLIE, YE CAN WASH THE WHEELS O' THIS CAR, - I'LL BE BACK IN A MINUTE.
THAT'S GREAT!
OCH! I'LL HELP LARRY AN' WASH THE WHOLE O' THE CAR!
HEY! I TELT YE TAE WASH THE WHEELS, NO' TAE SCOOT AT ME THROUGH THE OPEN WINDOWS!
AW JINGS! I'M AWFY SORRY, LARRY! AN' I WIS TRYIN' TAE BE HELPFUL!
WEEL, THERE'S SOMEONE AT THE FRONT, SEE WHIT HE WANTS WHILE I GET DRIED
QUICK! TWO GALLONS, - I'M IN A HURRY!
YJ 2474
HURRY UP, YE LAZY PUP!
YES SIR, COMING SIR!
TWA GALLONS, MISTER!
THAT'LL BE 3/7 SIR!
ALL RIGHT, TELL YOUR BOSS I'LL HAND IN THE MONEY AND THE COUPON ON MY WAY BACK!
DID YE GET HIS MONEY?
NA! BUT IT'LL BE ALL RIGHT!
POOL
DID A CAR, YJ 2474, STOP HERE FOR A FILL UP?
AYE, I PIT TWA GALLONS IN HIS TANK!
OH MY! THAT THIEF HAS GOT CLEAR AWAY WITH MY CAR!
AH, BUT I SPOTTED IT WISNA HIS CAR FRAE THE NUMBER, YOU'LL FIND HIM JUIST ROOND THE CORNER. WHIT I PIT IN HIS TANK WIS TWA GALLONS O' WATER!
IT'LL BE A NICE JOB FOR YOU, LARRY, TO EMPTY MY TANK OF THE WATER, BUT IT'S WORTH IT NOT TO LOSE MY CAR OR GET IT WRECKED!
AND HERE'S SOMETHING TO YOU, SON!

The Sunday Post 10th December 1939

HUH! YE'RE JUST LIKE A FAT GERMAN!
AH, GOSH! HERE'S THE TEACHER!
BOYS, BOYS! I WON'T HAVE THIS FIGHTING! WAIT TILL I GET YOU IN SCHOOL!
I FOUND WILLIAM AND ROBERT FIGHTING IN THE STREET TODAY! NOW THIS IS VERY WRONG! BOYS SHOULD NOT BE QUARRELSOME, BUT GO TO AND FROM SCHOOL QUIETLY AND PEACEFULLY!

1940

4
Nero's Baking Comes in Handy—See It Mends the Wall Just Dandy.
PLEMENT TO THE SUNDAY POST. APRIL 17, 1938.
NERO AND ZERO
THE ROLLICKING ROMANS
HAVE A HOT CROSS BUN O COMRADE! I'VE JUST MADE THEM!
I'LL TRY THE SMALL ONE!
?
BAH! THOU MUST HAVE MADE THEM WITH CEMENT!
LOOK WHAT THOU HAST DONE!
SOFTY SIMPKINS
THE VERY JOB FOR ME!
DEEDS & CO SOLICITORS
SMART OFFICE BOY WANTED
AH WELL! I'LL GIVE YOU A TRIAL— HERE IS THE OFFICE KEY— MIND YOU'RE HERE FIRST IN THE—MORNING!
I MUST BE FIRST! I MUST BE FIRST!
DAFT AS EVER
I MUST BE FIRST!
I MUST BE - SNORE - FIRST - I MUST BE Z-ZZ-Z
ZZZ
DEEDS & CO SOLICITORS
ZZZ
DEEDS & CO SOLICITORS
WELL! I WONDER IF THAT NEW BOY HAS ARRIVED YET?
SNORE ZZZ-Z
A FEW LINES MAKE A LAUGH
MY FATHER GETS A WARM RECEPTION WHEREVER HE GOES!
HE MUST BE VERY POPULAR
TO SCHOOL
NO, IT'S NOT THAT. YOU SEE HE'S A FIREMAN!
24

Fun Section Friends

The Broons and Oor Wullie weren't the only comic strips to appear in the Sunday Post's Fun Section during the 1930s and 1940s. Many others ran for years but without achieving the iconic status of Wullie and the Broons. This collection of strips dates from 1938.

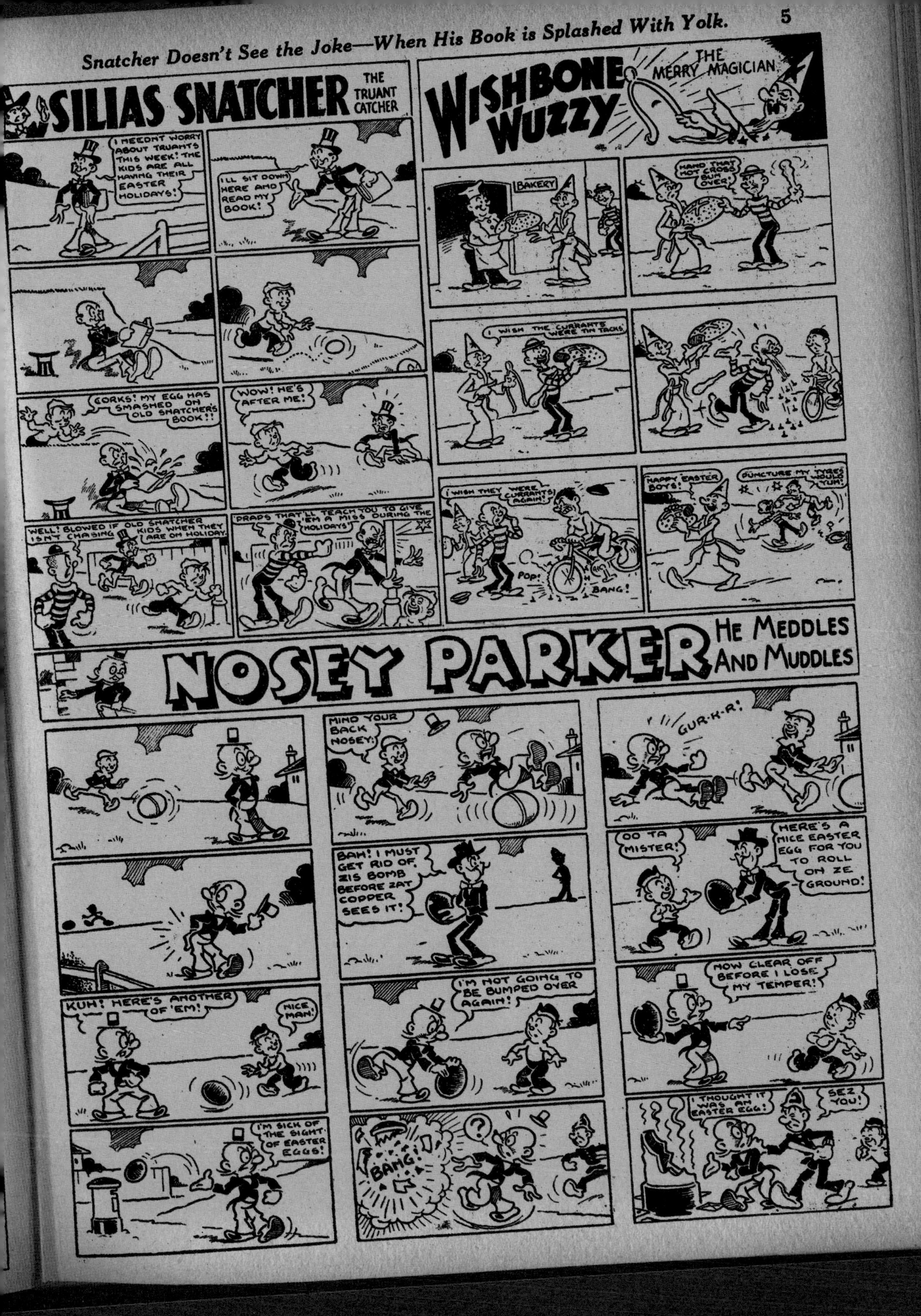
SILIAS SNATCHER
THE TRUANT CATCHER
I NEEDN'T WORRY ABOUT TRUANTS THIS WEEK! THE KIDS ARE ALL HAVING THEIR EASTER HOLIDAYS!
I'LL SIT DOWN HERE AND READ MY BOOK!
CORKS! MY EGG HAS SMASHED ON OLD SNATCHER'S BOOK!!
WOW! HE'S AFTER ME!
WELL! BLOWED IF OLD SNATCHER ISN'T CHASING KIDS WHEN THEY ARE ON HOLIDAY.
'PRAPS THAT'LL TEACH YOU TO GIVE 'EM A MISS DURING THE HOLIDAYS!'
WISHBONE WUZZY
THE MERRY MAGICIAN
BAKERY
HAND THAT HOT CROSS BUN OVER!
I WISH THE CURRANTS WERE TIN TACKS!
I WISH THEY WERE CURRANTS AGAIN!
POP!
BANG!
HAPPY EASTER BOYS!
PUNCTURE MY TYRES WOULD YUH!
NOSEY PARKER
HE MEDDLES AND MUDDLES
MIND YOUR BACK NOSEY!
GUR-R-R!
BAH! I MUST GET RID OF ZIS BOMB BEFORE ZAT COPPER SEES IT!
OO TA MISTER!
HERE'S A NICE EASTER EGG FOR YOU TO ROLL ON ZE GROUND!
KUH! HERE'S ANOTHER OF 'EM!
NICE MAN!
I'M NOT GOING TO BE BUMPED OVER AGAIN!
NOW CLEAR OFF BEFORE I LOSE MY TEMPER!
I'M SICK OF THE SIGHT OF EASTER EGGS!
BANG!
?
I THOUGHT IT WAS AN EASTER EGG!
SEZ YOU!

OOR WULLIE 1936-1946

HUH! YE'RE JUST LIKE A FAT GERMAN!
AW, GOSH! HERE'S THE TEACHER!
BOYS, BOYS! I WON'T HAVE THIS FIGHTING! WAIT TILL I GET YOU IN SCHOOL!
I FOUND WILLIAM AND ROBERT FIGHTING IN THE STREET TODAY! NOW THIS IS VERY WRONG! BOYS SHOULD NOT BE QUARRELSOME, BUT GO TO AND FROM SCHOOL QUIETLY AND PEACEFULLY!
AND NOW FOR A FEW GENERAL KNOWLEDGE QUESTIONS — WILLIAM, WHAT IS A SERGEANT?
PLEASE MISS, MY UNCLE WATTIE'S A SERGEANT! HE HAS THREE STRIPES AN' HE KEEPS ORDER AMONGST THE SOJERS - YE SEE HE KEEPS THEM QUIET AN' PEACEFUL!
EXCUSE ME, MISS SMITH! BUT THE HEADMASTER WANTS YOU!
WELL, WILLIAM, AS YOU KNOW ALL ABOUT SERGEANTS, YOU'LL KEEP ORDER IN THE CLASS TILL I COME BACK!
YES, MISS
NOW SIT UP AN' BEHAVE!
HUH! YOU COULDNA KEEP ORDER FOR TOFFEE! YE COULDNA EVEN KEEP WHITE MICE!
BE QUIET! - SILENCE! I COMMAND YOU!
RASP
STOP THAT FIGHTING! — WOW!
CLONK
WHO THREW THIS BOOK AT ME?
I DID, YE WEE TWERP!
WEEL, I MEAN TO HAE PEACE AN' ORDER HERE EVEN IF I HAE TAE FECHT THE LOT O' YE!
LOOK OUT LADS! HERE'S THE TEACHER!
I MANAGED TAE KEEP ORDER, MISS! THEY'RE A' QUIET!
GOOD, WILLIAM! NOW BOYS THE HEADMASTER WILL BE HERE IN A FEW MOMENTS!
THIS IS FLIGHT-LIEUTENANT WILSON, ONE OF OUR OLD PUPILS, HE HAS WON THE D.F.C. AND HE'S GOING TO TALK TO YOU!
HOORAY!
CHEERS
I'M GLAD TO SEE SUCH A FINE LOT OF YOUNG WARRIORS! I'M SURE YOU'RE ALL REAL TOUGH LADS WITH THE FIGHTING SPIRIT — NO CISSY NONSENSE ABOUT YOU, I CAN SEE THAT BY YOUR BLACK EYES — YOU'RE THE KIND OF LADS WE WANT —
AND NOW, BOYS, YOU CAN ALL HAVE THE AFTERNOON OFF IN HONOUR OF OUR VISITOR!
WELL, I WON'T STOP THEM FIGHTING NOW, AFTER WHAT FLIGHT-LIEUTENANT WILSON SAID!

The Sunday Post 2nd June 1940

JINGS! I COULD GO A FINE JUICY KIPPER FOR SUPPER WHIT ABOOT IT, MAW?
I'VE NANE IN THE HOOSE. I COULD GIE YE BILED HAM, OR A FRIED EGG, A MEALY PUDDEN OR TINNED SALMON, IF YE WANT A KIPPER YE'LL NEED TAE GAE OOT AN' BUY ANE, YE'VE JUIST TIME!
WHAUR ARE YE GOIN' PAW?
ARE YE NO' HAEIN' YER SUPPER?
AW-A-JUIST OOT A MESSAGE!
WHIT'S FOR SUPPER, MAW?
YE CAN HAE BILED HAM, FRIED EGG, MEALY PUDDEN OR SALMON, OR—
AW! I'D RAITHER HAE A KIPPER, NICE AN' TASTY!
SIT DOON, PAW, AN' HAE SOME BILED HAM!
NA! NA! AH'M NO-ER-HUNGRY—FOR BILED HAM!
THIS SALMON'S AN AWFY CAULD FEED!
SO ARE ARE THESE SARDINES! IF WE ONLY HAD SOME NICE KIPPERS IN THE HOOSE!
HERE, PAW, I CANNA DAE YER KIPPERS AN' A' THE FAMILY RAVENOUS FOR THEM! THERE'D BE A RIOT!
I KEN,— I'LL TAK A PAN AN' JOE'S PRIMUS STOVE AN' FRY THEM IN THE WASHIN HOOSE!!
WHAUR ARE YE AFF TAE, NOO?
AW,— JUIST OOT FOR— ER— FRESH AIR!
THIS IS GOIN' TAE BE GOOD. I'LL NEED TAE GO UP FOR SOME BREID, THOUGH. I FORGOT ABOOT THAT!
SIZZLE
GIE ME A BIT BREAD, WILL YE!
HERE, THERE'S ONLY THE HEEL O' THE LOAF LEFT!
WHIT'S IT FOR? YE SAID YE WISNA HUNGRY!
JINGS! CRIVVENS!! MICHTY ME!!!— THEY CATS HAVE EATEN A' MA KIPPERS!!
HUH! A' I'VE GOT FOR MA SUPPER IS THIS HEEL AN' A BIT AULD CHEESE OOT'N THE MOOSE TRAP!!
AH WEEL, YE SHOULDNA HAE BEEN SAE GREEDY ABOOT THEY KIPPERS, PAW!

The Sunday Post 7th January 1940

OOR WULLIE 1936-1946

JINGS! LOOK AT THE CLOCK, I'LL BE AT SCHOOL TOO EARLY— I'LL GO A ROOND ABOOT ROAD!
HULLO, MISTER! WHIT'S THIS TAR FOR?
NEVER YOU MIND. AWA YE GO!
TAR
WHIT ARE YE DAEN' DOON IN THAT HOLE?— OOH SORRY!
TAR
AW CRIVVENS IT'S TWENTY FIVE PAST NINE— NOW I'M OWER LATE FOR THE SCHOOL!
OCH! I'LL JUIST HIDE MA BAG AN' TAK THE MORNIN' AFF!
CAN I HELP YE, MISTER?
O.K. MIND MY LADDER AND STUFF WHILE I GO A MESSAGE!
H-M! I COULD GET ON WI' THIS JOB MASEL', IT LOOKS EASY! IT'LL SAVE THE PUIR MAN'S TIME!
WILSON'S GOLDEN
I'D BETTER GET BACK TAE MA BILL POSTIN'— I HOPE THAT BAIRN HASNAE BEEN MESSIN' WI' MA PASTE!
SEE! — I'VE BEEN HELPIN' YE!
DRINK SMITH'S BOTTLED
SOAP
SOAP
IT MAKES YOUR HAIR CURLY!
WILSON'S GOLDEN FRUITADE
WASHES YOUR CLOTHES AS WHITE AS SNOW!
JUST TRY IT!
LADIES AND GENTS OUTFITTER
WHAT A TOPPER
THAT'S TURNED IT AFF!
SEE IF I CAN TURN IT ON AGAIN!
WHA DID THAT?
WHISTLE
IT WIS HIM!
THAT AFTERNOON
SCHOOL
NOTE FOR TEACHER
Please excuse William for being absent this forenoon as I was sick (signed) My Father
COME HERE, MY BOY!

The Sunday Post 16th June 1940

DINNER TIME.
YE'RE WANTED ON THE PHONE IN SOUTAR THE GROCER'S SHOP MRS BROON!
I WONDER WHIT IT'S FOR,— I HOPE NAETHIN'S WRANG!
AT THE GROCER'S
YES,— IT'S ME, BUT MICHTY! JINGS!— I'M NO' SURE IF I CAN COME!
JINGS! IS THAT MRS BROON GETTIN' A PHONE CALL?
AYE! A MAN'S VOICE ASKED FOR MRS BROON— AT LEAST IT SOUNDED LIKE MRS BROON,— SO I SENT UP FOR HER!
WELL, I NEVER EXPECTED THIS— BUT I'LL SEE!— FANCY YOU RINGIN' ME UP, JOHNNY HUTTON!
WID YE BELIEVE IT! DAE YE MIND JOHNNY HUTTON?— HE RANG ME UP AN' ASKED ME TAE A DANCE THE NICHT! I USED TAE KEN HIM TWENTY YEARS AGO,— WHIT'LL I DAE?
ACH! YE SHOULD GO— IT'LL BE GUID FUN! FORBYE I'LL GET A NICHT OOT WI' THE BOYS!
FANCY MAW GETTIN' AFF AN' ME,— I'VE ONLY BEEN ASKED TAE ONE DANCE IN THE LAST SEVEN YEARS!
THAT NIGHT.
THIS IS A FUNNY BUSINESS,— ARE YE SURE THE PHONE WIS FOR YOU, MAW?
OF COURSE! DAE YE THINK I DINNA KEN JOHNNY HUTTON?
KNOCK KNOCK
HULLO! THERE'S A KNOCK AT THE DOOR— I'LL SEE WHA IT IS!
WHO ARE YOU?
I'M JOHNNY HUTTON, BUT IT WIS MISS BROON I ASKED FOR ON THE PHONE!
I KEN WHIT'S HAPPENED,— IT'S YOUR FAITHER THAT MAW KENT TWENTY YEARS AGO!
AYE, AN' THE GROCER MADE A MISTAKE AN' SENT FOR MRS BROON INSTEAD O' MISS BROON!
I SUPPOSE IT WAS ME YOU MEANT TO ASK TO THE DANCE!
JINGS! I'M REAL DISAPPOINTED!
AYE! AN' YOU A' DRESSED UP FOR THE DANCE, MAW!
YE DAFT DUMB-CLUCK! HOW DID YE MAKE A MISTAKE LIKE THAT!
BUT I THOCHT IT WIS YOU SPEAKIN', MAGGIE!
OCH! NEVER MIND— I'LL TELL YE WHIT— WE'LL A' GANG TAE THE DANCE— AN' WE'LL GET THE REAL JOHNNY HUTTON TAE COME ANA'!
AT THE DANCE
JINGS! LOOK AT PAW'S FOOT WORK!
GEE! MAW'S FAIR ENJOYIN' HERSEL'!
HOO ABOOT ME TAKIN' YE HAME?

The Sunday Post 14th January 1940

HULLO, ALF, — WAITIN' FOR MABEL?
GO AWAY, YOU DIRTY LITTLE SCRUFF AND MIND YOUR OWN BUSINESS!
JINGS! IT BEATS ME HOW MABEL WILSON GANGS OUT WI' A SOUR BLOKE LIKE YON — HA! — THERE'S MABEL NOW!
HULLO, WULLIE, HAE YE SEEN A BOY FRIEND O' MINE WAITIN' FOR ME?
AYE, THERE'S A CHAP ROOND THE CORNER WI' A WEE MOUSTACHE, I'LL TAK YE TAE HIM!
HERE'S YER BOY FRIEND, MABEL!
YOU AGAIN!
OH, AH — ER — MABEL I WAS TO TAKE YOU TO THE FLICKS TO-NIGHT, BUT I'M — AH — WELL I'M BROKE!
OH, ALFRED! WHAT A NUISANCE!
COULD YOU NOT BORROW TWO OR THREE SHILLINGS SOMEWHERE?
GOSH! — ER — I DON'T THINK SO!
HEY, MISTER! I KEN HOW YE CAN GET THE MONEY!
OH, IT'S YOU IS IT — WELL, HOW?
WEEL, ME AN' MA PAL, BOB CAN THROW MUD A' OWER MABEL'S FAITHER'S CAR — THEN YOU CAN OFFER TAE CLEAN IT FOR FIVE BOB THEN ME AN' BOB WILL CLEAN IT FOR TWA SHILLINGS, SEE?
THAT'S A GOOD IDEA, ALF!
GO ON, ALF, TELL PAW HIS CAR'S ALL MUDDY, AN' THAT YOU'LL CLEAN IT FOR FIVE SHILLINGS!
NOW WE'LL START AN' CLEAN IT AGAIN!
GOSH! ALF'S A LONG TIME COMING BACK!
YES, I'LL CLEAN THE CAR FOR YOU IN A JIFFY — I LOVE CLEANING CARS.
WELL, MY LAD, GO AHEAD! HERE'S FIVE SHILLINGS!
GOSH! I BET THOSE KIDS HAVE GOT THE CAR CLEANED BY NOW. I'LL PLAY A TRICK ON THEM!
WELL, WE'VE CLEANED THE CAR — WHIT ABOOT OOR TWA BOB?
HAR! HAR! THAT'S A JOKE ON YOU KIDS! MABEL'S FATHER DOESN'T WANT HIS CAR CLEANED! HE SAID IT'S SURE TO RAIN TO-NIGHT, SO YOU'VE WORKED FOR NOTHING!
IT'S ALL RIGHT, MABEL, I GOT FIVE SHILLINGS FOR CLEANING THE CAR, WE'LL KEEP IT TO OURSELVES!
WOW!
WHY, YOU DIRTY DOUBLE-CROSSER! TAKE THAT!
SMACK
COME ON, GIVE ME THAT MONEY OR I'LL TELL MY FATHER YOU GOT IT WITHOUT WORKING FOR IT!
JINGS! HE'S BEEN TRYIN' TAE SWINDLE US!
SAY, IT'S A GUID JOB WE HAD SOME MUD LEFT!
AYE!
TAK' THAT, YE TWISTER!
COME ON, WULLIE AN' BOB! WE'LL GO TO THE PICTURES WI' THAT FIVE SHILLINGS!

The Sunday Post 11th August 1940

AW! WHIT A BONNY PHOTIE O' GRAN'PAW, WHEN HE WIS YOUNG! I WISH MEN WID GROW BEARDS NOWADAYS! YE KEN, I COULD JUIST FALL FOR A TALL HANDSOME MAN WI' A BLACK BEARD!
WEEL, I KEN A BLOKE JUIST LIKE THAT, DAPHNE, - WID YE LIKE TAE MEET HIM? - I'LL BRING HIM ROOND THE MORN'S NICHT!
DAPHNE'S NUTS!
NEXT NIGHT!
HOW DO YOU DO, MISS BROWN!
MEET MISTER - ER - HENRY!
OH, MY! PLEASED TAE MEETCHA, MR HENRY!
DAPHNE, YE'VE AYE BEEN A GUID SISTER TAE ME AN' I DINNA LIKE SEEIN' YE BEIN' TA'EN A LEN O' BY YON BLOKE -! HE'S A FAKE! I HAPPEN TAE KEN THAT HE'S GOT FALSE TEETH, A GLASS EYE, A WIG, A WIDDEN LEFT LEG, AN' HIS BEARD'S FALSE!
OH HORACE! IS THAT RICHT? - AW JINGS! YE'RE NO' KIDDIN' ME, ARE YE? - AH, WEEL, I'LL SUNE FIND OOT FOR MASEL'!
COFFEE AND CHOCOLATE BISCUITS FOR THE BLOKE!
THINKS I'LL GIE HIM SOME O' MY HOME-MADE TREACLE TOFFEE TAE SEE IF HIS FALSE TEETH GET STUCK WI' IT!
OH, MR HENRY, YOU MUST TRY SOME OF MY TOFFEE! I MADE IT MYSELF!
OH THANKS, MISS BROWN!
AW JINGS, DAPHNE, YE WIDNA GIE US ONY WHEN WE ASKED YE!
THINKS:- JINGS! THE TOFFEE'S NO' GETTIN' AHENT HIS PLATE AT A'!
GOOD JOB I DON'T HAVE FALSE TEETH, MISS BROWN, OR THIS TOFFEE WOULD MAKE THEM STICK TOGETHER!
CHEW
THINKS:- HORACE WIS A' WRANG WHEN HE SAID MR HENRY HAD FALSE TEETH! BUT NOW I'LL SEE IF HE WIS RICHT ABOOT THE WIG!
PULL
YOW!! OH GEE! - MISS BROON - WHIT - WHAT ARE YOU DOING?
BEN THE HOOSE!
HUH! WAIT TILL I GET THAT HORACE! YON WISNA A WIG - BUT MEBBE HE REALLY HAS A WIDDEN LEG THOUGH! NOW IF I SOCK HIM OWER THE LEFT LEG WI' THIS BROOM, AN' IT DOESNA HURT HIM, I'LL KEN IT'S A WIDDEN LEG!
OH MAW! THIS BROOM WIS LYIN' ABOOT, WHAUR SHALL I PIT IT? - OH, SORRY, MR HENRY, - DID I HURT YE?
OOH!!
THINKS CRIVVENS! IT'S NO' A WIDDEN LEG!
JINGS, JOE! - I'M FED UP PLAYIN' THIS GAME! I'VE BEEN HALF PISENED WI' DAPHNE'S ROTTEN TOFFEE, SHE ABOOT SCALPED ME, - SHE'LL HAE ME A CRIPPLE AFORE SHE'S DONE - SO TAK THIS, YE AGGRAVATIN' BESOM!
WHISPER--
JINGS! SO THAT'S WHA IT IS!
I'LL PULL YER BEARD AFF FOR THAT, YE BIG LOUT - JINGS! - IT'S HEN!!

The Sunday Post 4th February 1940

OOR WULLIE 1936-1946

THIS IS THE NICHT FOR YER BATH, WULLIE!
ACH! MAW! I'M NO NEEDIN' A BATH!
YE ARE SO, GO ON AN' GET ON WITH IT!
LET'S SHAM THE SCRUBBIN' BRUSH IS A GERMAN BATTLESHIP —
— THEN OWER COMES A BRITISH BOMBER — ZO-OM!!
SOAP
BANG! - CRASH! — THE PLANE DROPS A BOMB ON IT!
AN' NOW ANOTHER BOMBER - AW JINGS! HERE'S MAW!
SO — THIS IS HOW YE BATH YERSEL?
YER KNEES AN' YER EARS ARE FILTHY! COME ON AN' I'LL DAE THEM PROPERLY!
BUT MAW I DID THEM!
OH! THAT'S SAIR — AN' THE WATER'S CAULD NOO!
WEEL, YE'VE GOT TAE BE CLEAN!
HALF AN HOUR LATER
JINGS, SOAPY! YE'RE AN AWFY MESS! HOO DAE YE NO' KEEP YERSEL' CLEAN?
AW! NUTS TAE YOU — TAK' THAT!
PUSH
PUSH ME IN THE MUD WID YE?
HUH! MEBBE THAT'LL TEACH HIM TAE KEEP CLEAN LIKE ME!
JINGS! YE'RE FILTHY AGAIN!
HERE'S A CHANCE FOR YE, WULLIE! MR. SMITH, DOON THE ROAD, WANTS A BOY TAE DAE AN HOUR'S WORK. HE CANNA GET A MAN TAE DAE IT—
BUT YE'RE AN AWFY MICKEY!
AYE! YE'LL NEED TAE CLEAN YERSEL' OR YE'LL NO' GET THE JOB - AWA' INTAE THE BATH!
AW JINGS! THIS IS TERRIBLE!
YE'RE FINE NOW — LIKE A NEW PIN!
YE WERE WANTIN' A BOY TAE DAE A JOB, MR SMITH?
YOU'LL DAE FINE YE'RE A SMART LOOKIN' LAD! COME ROOND THE BACK!
I WANT A' THAT COAL SHOVELLED INTAE BUCKETS AN' CARTED INTAE MA CELLAR - AN' I'LL GIE YE HALF-A-CROON!
THANKS WULLIE - THAT'S VERY GOOD - HERE'S YER HALF-CROON!
THANKS, MISTER SMITH!
CRIVVENS! WHAUR HAE YE BEEN?
SHOVELLIN' COAL!
YE'LL NEED A BATH AT ONCE!

The Sunday Post 18th August 1940

WEEL, DAPHNE, I SEE A LETTER COMING TAE YOU IN YOUR CUP,—FROM A GENTLEMAN, AN' HE'S TAE TELL YE JUIST WHIT HE THINKS O' YE! AN' MAGGIE, THE TEA LEAVES IN YOUR CUP TELL ME THAT YE'RE TAE HAE A LOT O' NEW GENTLEMEN FRIENDS TAE SEE YE THIS WEEK!
AW JINGS! SHE'S HAVERIN'! THAT'S JUIST A LOT O' TRASH!
COME ON, GRAN'PAW, MRS SCRIMGEOUR'LL HAE TAE READ YOUR CUP, TAE!
AH-HA! I SEE BY YER TEA CUP, SOME FOLKS ARE GOIN' TAE MAK' AN AWFUL FOOL O' YE AFORE THE WEEK'S OOT!
WHIT?—HUH—! THERE'S NAEBODY GAUN TAE MAK' A FOOL OOT O' ME!
JINGS! I'LL HAE A RARE JOKE ON DAPHNE AN' MAGGIE,— I'LL MAK' WHIT THE FORTUNE WIFIE SAID ABOOT THEM COME TRUE!
NEXT DAY
AW, MAW— MRS SCRIMGEOUR WIS RICHT!— I'VE GOT A LETTER, BUT LISTEN TAE IT— "DEAR DAPHNE, WHIT AN UGLY MUG YE'VE GOT! IT'S THE WORST IN GLEBE STREET, AN' HOO CAN YE NO' DAE SOMETHIN' TAE GET YER FAT DOON? IF IT WISNA FOR YER SNUB NOSE YE'D BE QUITE GUID LOOKIN' IF YE WISNA CROSS-EYED! I'D ASK YE OOT WI' ME BUT I WIDNA LIKE FOLKS TAE THINK I WIS GAUN STEADY WI' AN ELEPHANT— YOURS RESPECTFULLY, TAM"
LATER
HULLO, MAGGIE! YER FORTUNE'S COME TRUE— FOUR LADS TAE SEE YE!!
I'VE BROCHT THAE YOUNG LADS TAE SEE YE, MAGGIE! THEY'RE A' KEEN ON DANCIN' AN' PAIRTIES!
OH BOY! SHE'S A HUM-DINGER!
NEXT DAY
WEEL, MAGGIE, YE GOT YER GENTLEMEN FRIENDS AS THE FORTUNE WIFIE SAID, AND DID YE GET THE LETTER, DAPHNE? I WROTE IT MASEL', I WIDNA SEE YE DISAPPOINTED— HA! HA!!
OCH! YE'RE AN AULD RASCAL, GRAN'PAW! YE WILL HAE YER WEE JOKE, O' COURSE. WE DINNA MIND!
WEEL, SEEIN' YE GOT THE LAUGH ON US, YE'LL HAE TAE LET US SHOW YE A NEW WAY TAE PLAY "POSTMAN'S KNOCK"!
I DINNA LIKE THIS NICE WAY THAE TWA ARE TAKIN' GRAN'PAW'S JOKE!
AY, HE'S IN FOR IT!
OCH AYE! I'M GAME FOR ONYTHING! I'M AYE READY FOR A BIT FUN!
WHEN WE SAY "READY", YOU RISE UP AN' WALK ROOND WI' US!
NOW KEEP YER HANDS STILL WHILE I TIE THEM!
HERE! WHIT ARE YE DAEIN'? YE'RE TAKIN' AN AWFY LANG TIME!
WHAUR ARE YE TAKIN' ME?— I'M GAUN DOON STAIRS— HERE! WHIT'S THE GAME
YOU'LL SEE WHEN WE TELL YE TAE TAK THE BLINDFOLD BANDAGE AFF!
SO YE SAID NAEBODY COULD MAK A FOOL O' YE, DID YE?— WEEL, THE FORTUNE WIFIE WIS RICHT WHEN SHE READ YER CUP!!
HEY TAM! LOOK AT THIS!

The Sunday Post 11th February 1940

HOW OFTEN AM I TAE TELL YE NO' TAE THROW TOWELS ON THE FLOOR AN' LEAVE SOAP IN THE WATTER, AN'—
THERE YE'VE LEFT MA SAW AN' MA HAMMER LYIN' OOT IN THE WET, AN' NAILS A' OWER THE PLACE!
NAILS
OCH! I'M AYE GETTIN' INTAE ROWS!
HULLO, WULLIE! WE'VE BEEN WORKIN' AT FORESTRY IN THE HIELAN'S — WE LIVED FOR A MONTH OORSEL'S!
AYE! WE DID A' OOR AIN COOKIN' AN' HOOSE-WORK!
JINGS! IT MUST BE RARE TAE GANG AWA' LIKE THAT AN' NO' HAE YER MITHER AN' FAITHER BOSSIN' YE ABOOT!
NOW, WULLIE, YE'LL TAK' THIS NOTE TAE YER AUNTY JESSIE AN' SAY WE'VE BEEN CALLED AWAY TAE MARY'S AN' WE'LL BE BACK THE MORN. SHE'LL PIT YE UP. NOW GET YER NIGHTY READY!
OCH! I'LL NO' GANG TAE MA AUNTIE'S — I'LL STAY BY MASEL'!
MAN, IT'S GRAND TAE BE ON YER AIN! I'LL SHAM I'M FAITHER AN' HAE A PIPE!
THIS IS THE LIFE!
POP
NEWS
OOH!!— I'M SICK!!
20 MINUTES LATER.
I'LL MAK' MA BED LIKE I WIS CAMPIN'!
IT TAK'S A BIT O' DOIN'!
NOO I'LL GET SOME GRUB!
THESE SARDINES TASTE QUEER LIKE— AN' MA TEA'S LIKE DISH WATTER!
SARDINES
I THINK I'LL GO TAE MA BED NOW— IT'S GETTIN' DARK!
AW JINGS! IT'S AWFY QUIET IN THE HOOSE MASEL— WHIT'S THAT?
OH MAW! MAW!! I'M FEART!!!
ACH! I'M GAUN TAE MA AUNT JESSIE'S — THIS IS OWER LONELY!
HULLO, AUNTIE JESSIE! MAW AN' PAW HAVE GONE TAE MARY'S — HERE'S A LETTER, LET'S IN!!
BUT YE'RE AWFY LATE IN COMIN' WULLIE!
OCH! I WIS BUSY TIDYIN' UP THE HOOSE AFORE I LEFT!
THERE YE ARE NOW, TUCKED UP NICELY IN BED!
I'M A FEARDIE-GOWK!!

The Sunday Post 1st September 1940

ACH! I'M AWA' OOT FOR A WALK IN THE COUNTRY — I LIKE TAE SEE NATURE — THE FLOO'ERS AN' THE BEES AN' THE BIRDS!
A' RICHT, TAK' CARE O' YERSEL'!
Z-Z-Z-Z
Z-Z-
CRIVVENS! THEY'RE NO' BEES! THEY'RE WASPS!
STING
Z-Z
OH DEAR! I'M STUNG! I'LL NEED TAE GET HAME QUICK AN' GET IODINE ON MA FACE OR SOMETHING!
SWELLING
HELLO, SANDY! CAN YE HELP A PUIR MAN THAT'S BEEN STUNG?
I DINNA KEN YE, AN' FORBYE I WIDNA GIE MONEY TAE AN AULD TRAMP!
HULLO LADDIES! LOOK AT MA PUIR FACE!
JINGS! WHIT AN UGLY AULD MANNIE!
AWA' YE GO, OR I'LL TELL MA FAITHER ON YE!
ME SCARED!
HELLO GIRLS—
HUH! THAT FUNNY FACED AULD MAN THINKS HE KENS ME!
THE BROONS CLOSSIE
H.B.
TAKE NO NOTICE!
HEY! YOU GET OOT O' HERE!
BUT I'M YER FAITHER!
CUT OOT THE FUNNY STUFF! I SURELY KEN MA AIN AULD MAN— COME ON!
AWA YE GO! GET OOT O' HERE!
BUT-BUT!
I'M LOOKIN' FOR BROON THAT STAYS HERE! HE'S A WEE FELLA' ABOUT YOUR SIZE — BUT NO' QUITE SAE UGLY! I'LL BASH HIM WHEN I GET HIM!
OH — ER — HE'S AWA UP THE STREET!
JINGS! NAEBODY WID KEN YE WI' A FACE LIKE THAT!
NO, AN' IT WIS A GUID JOB TOO, THAT BIG JOCK SMITH DIDNA KEN ME!

The Sunday Post 30th June 1940

NOW, BOYS! HURRY, OR YOU'LL BE LATE FOR SCHOOL!
YES, SIR!
WHISPER.- JINGS! THAT NEW HEAD-MASTER'S A TOUGH GUY!
HE WIDNA BE SAFT WI' US IF HE COPPED US MISBEHAVIN'!
HULLO, JOE! WHIT'S YER HURRY?
I'M GAUN TAE SEE THE NAZI BOMBER THAT CRASHED IN THE FIELD AT DOWNHALL!
JINGS! I WISH WE COULD GO — BUT OOR NEW HEIDMASTER WID TAK THE SKIN AFF O' YE IF YE PLAYED TRUANT!
HERE! I'VE GOT THE VERY IDEA — I'LL BLEED MA NOSE WI' RED INK AN' TURN SICK IN SCHOOL AN' YOU TWA'LL HAE TAE TAK' ME HAME!
JINGS! THAT'S A RARE IDEA!
IN SCHOOL
WHISPER.- PEY ATTENTION TAE THE TEACHER WHILE I DAE THE RED INK!
OH, PLEASE, MISS — MA NOSE'S BLEEDIN' AN' I'M FEELING QUEER!
OH DEAR! SOMEBODY HELP HIM!
OH! PUIR WULLIE!
WE'LL TAK' HIM HAME, MISS! — WE KEN WHAUR HE BIDES!
HAUD UP, NOW, WULLIE! DINNA FAINT!
SCHOOL
WE'LL FAIRLY CROW OWER THE ITHER LADS THE MORN, WHEN WE TELL THEM ABOOT THIS!
JINGS! I CANNA RIN FOR LAUGHING!
HEY! WHIT ARE YOU LADS DAEIN' OOT O' SCHOOL?
OH—ER, YE SEE, WULLIE'S SICK!
QUICK, HAUD ME UP!
ON THE WAY TO THE BOMBER
AW JINGS! HERE'S THE HEADMASTER! LET'S HIDE IN THIS CRATE 'TILL HE'S GONE!
HA! HERE'S A NICE BOX TAE SIT ON WHILE I'M FISHIN'!
LISTEN! — FOOTSTEPS! — SH—SH! MAYBE IT'S THE HEADMASTER!
YE'VE NO SEEN THREE YOUNG LADDIES ROOND HERE, HAVE YE? ANE O' EM WIS SUPPOSED TAE BE SICK— BUT I HAE MA DOUBTS!
I BET THEY'LL BE PLAYIN' TRUANT — THEY NEED A SPANKIN'!
JINGS! WE'VE BEEN STUCK HERE TWA HOURS NOW AN' CANNA GET OOT! THIS BLOKE WID TELL THE POLIS!
LOOK! THE BOTTOM O' THE BOX IS BROKEN LET'S PUSH IT OWER!
HELP!
SLIDE
JUIST KEEP IN THE BOX 'TILL WE GET ROOND THE CORNER SO AS THE BLOKE'LL NO SEE WHA TIPPED HIM IN THE WATTER!
JINGS! THAT BOX HAS GOT FEET AN' LEGS!
NOW TAE SEE THE NAZI BOMBER!
HULLO! ARE YOU LADS LOOKIN' FOR THE NAZI BOMBER? — WEEL YE'RE TOO LATE, AN RAF LORRY TOWED IT AWA' TEN MINUTES AGO!
AW CRIVVENS!
NEXT DAY
HARD LUCK ON YOU THREE! THE NEW HEAD-MASTER LET US ALL OFF FOR THE AFTERNOON TAE GO AN' SEE THE NAZI BOMBER!
IT WIS A' YOUR FAULT!
AYE! YOU AN' YER RED INK!
IT'S A REAL ANE THIS TIME!

The Sunday Post 20th October 1940

ALL RIGHT, YOU'LL COME UP WITH ME TO OUR HOUSE AT SEVEN TO-NIGHT! I'LL MEET YOU AT 6-30!
YES, THANK YOU VERY MUCH MRS. SMITH AND I WOULD LIKE TO MEET YOUR FAMILY!
AT THE BROONS
HERE YE ARE, THAT'S A' THE DIRTY TOWELS IN THE HOOSE!
THANK YOU, THE TOWEL CLEANING SERVICE WILL LET YOU HAVE THEM BACK TOMORROW!
TOWEL CLEANING SERVICE
I GAVE A' THE TOWELS I COULD SEE TAE THE GIRL FROM THE TOWEL CLEANING SERVICE, MAW! THEY MAK' A RARE JOB — OH! HULLO, HEN, HULLO, JOE!
MY GOODNESS A' THE REST O' THE TOWELS ARE IN THE WASHING! I'LL NEED TAE GO AN' BUY SOME NOW!
WE'VE COME FOR BATHS— WE'VE BEEN SHOVELLIN' COAL!
QUICK! GIMME A TOWEL!
THERE'RE NAE TOWELS! HERE, TAK' THIS DUSTER!
WE'VE BEEN CLEANIN' OOR BIKES. WE WANT A WASH!
THERE ARE NAE TOWELS! YE'LL NEED TAE WAIT TILL MAW COMES BACK!
JINGS! THIS DUSTER'S NO AS GOOD AS A TOWEL!
LOOK, PAW'S FACE IS DIRTIER THAN EVER, NOO, WI' THAT FILTHY DUSTER!
AYE! IT'S A' DAPHNE'S BLAME!
HOORAY! NO WASH!
ME PLAY MUD PIES! ME FA' IN!
OH, DEAR YOU NEED A BATH— BUT WE'VE NAE TOWELS!
WE CANNA LET DAPHNE GET AWA' WI' THIS!
HA! HA! WE'VE A' GOT BLACK FACES, NOW!
WE'VE A' GOT BLACK FACES EXCEPT YOU— AN' I DINNA SEE WHY YOU SHOULD BE LET AFF WI' A CLEAN FACE!
HEY! STOP IT!
AYE, SEEIN' IT'S HER FAULT WE CANNA GET CLEANED!
IT SERVES HER RICHT!
THE VISITORS ARRIVE
I'VE GOT THE TOWELS — OH, MY, WHIT'S A' THIS?
YE'RE OWER LATE, MAW! LOOK WHA'S HERE!
OH—AH—ER— THIS IS MY FAMILY!
BLUSH
PARDON MY MAKE-UP!

The Sunday Post 22nd September 1940

12 MIDNIGHT, DEC 31ST 1940
COLIN McLEOD, THE PIPER IS COMIN' TAE FIRST FOOT US — THAT'LL BE HIM AT THE DOOR NOO!
HAPPY NEW YEAR MA WEE LAMB!
KNOCK KNOCK
SAME TAE YOU, MAW!
HAPPY NEW YEAR, A'BODY! AM I YER FIRST FUT?
AYE. COLIN!
I'LL GIE YE A TUNE ON MA PIPES, BUT THEY'LL NEED A WEE DRAM FIRST— THEY AYE PLAY BETTER WI' A WEE DRAM!
HERE YE ARE THEN, COLIN!
WAIL MOAN
NOW I'M AFF ON A FIRST FUTTIN' EXPEDITION AN' I'D LIKE TAE TAK' WULLIE WI' ME FOR LUCK! WULL YE LET HIM COME?
AW, MAW! PLEASE LET ME
A' RICHT, BUT TAK CARE!
WE'RE GAUN TAE FIRST FUT SANDY LOW!
HAPPY NEW YEAR, COLIN, COME AWA' IN!
I'VE BROCHT MA PIPES AN' WULLIE ALANG WI' ME!
GIE MA PIPES A WEE DRAM AN' I'LL GIE YE A TUNE!
NOW WE'RE TAE FIRST FUT MY BRITHER! WE'RE AYE FECHTIN' BUT WE AYE MAK' IT UP AT NEW YEAR— HE GOT MAD AT ME LAST NEW YEAR WHEN I SAID HE NEEDED A BATH!
HA! HA!
HAPPY NEW YEAR, MURDOCH! I'VE COME TAE MAK' IT UP AN' WE'LL BE FRIENDS AGAIN! I'M SORRY I SAID YE NEEDED A BATH!
AW WEEL, A GUID NEW YEAR TAE YE AN' WE'LL NO QUARREL AGAIN!
MR McLEOD AYE GIES HIS PIPES A WEE DRINK AFORE HE PLAYS!
HERE'S LEMONADE, WE'LL TRY THAT IN THEM!
THAT SEEMS AN AWFU' LOT TAE PIT IN — YE'VE EMPTIED THE BOTTLE!
GIE'S A TUNE COLIN AFORE YE GO, AN' MAK' IT A FRIENDSHIP TUNE!
SO YE STILL THINK WE NEED A BATH! HUH— SQUIRTIN' WATER A' OWER US LIKE THAT!— IT WIS A TRICK!
AW, PLEASE. MR McLEOD— DINNA BLAME COLIN— WE PIT LEMONADE IN HIS PIPES TAE GIE THEM A DRINK!
JINGS! WE NEARLY HAD ANITHER FECHT— ON NEW YEAR'S MORNIN' TAE!
THAE BAIRNS!
WEEL, HERE'S WULLIE BACK SAFE AN' SOUND— WE HAD A GRAND TIME!
A HAPPY NEW YEAR TAE A' YOU FOWKS!
Wullie

The Sunday Post 29th December 1940

HULLO, SANTA! ARE YE THERE? WEEL, I WANT A TOY PIANO AN' A—!
AN' I WANT A TROMBONE, A REAL YIN, MIND!
AN' I WANT A MOOTH ORGAN AN' A MELODEON LIKE JOE'S!
DAE YE HEAR THAT? THEY WANT TOYS TAE MAK' A NOISE WI'!
I THINK WE'D BETTER SEE SANTY CLAUS AN' TELL HIM TAE BRING NICE QUIET TOYS!
NA! NA! WE HAD ENOUGH RACKET LAST CHRISTMAS WI' THEIR DRUMS AN' TRUMPETS!
CHRISTMAS EVE
AYE, SANTA CLAUS HAS GIVEN THE BAIRNS THE RICHT SORT O' PRESENTS THIS YEAR! QUIET BOOKS AN' GAMES!
CHRISTMAS MORNING
OOH-OOH! MA STOCKIN'S FU'!
THAT'S RICHT, LIFT IT DOON!
OH! JINGS! THE DANDY MONSTER COMIC! OOH! AN' SNAKES AN' LADDERS!
AN' WHIT DID SANTA BRING YOU?
A JIG-SAW PUZZLE AN' THE BEANO COMIC AN' AN ORANGE AN' A NEW PENNY, MAW!
HOW NICE!
CHRISTMAS NIGHT
A MERRY CHRISTMAS TAE YE A'!
HULLO, GRAN'PAW! MERRY CHRISTMAS!
I'VE BROCHT THE BAIRNS SOME CHRISTMAS PRESENTS! HERE'S A TRUMPET FOR YOU, AN' A DRUM FOR YOU, AN—
HOORAY! A MOOTH ORGAN WI' BELLS ON IT!
GEE! A DRUM!
RACKET
SMASH!!
HAMMER
THUMP
SCREECH
WAIL
BLAST

The Sunday Post 22nd December 1940

Oor Toons!

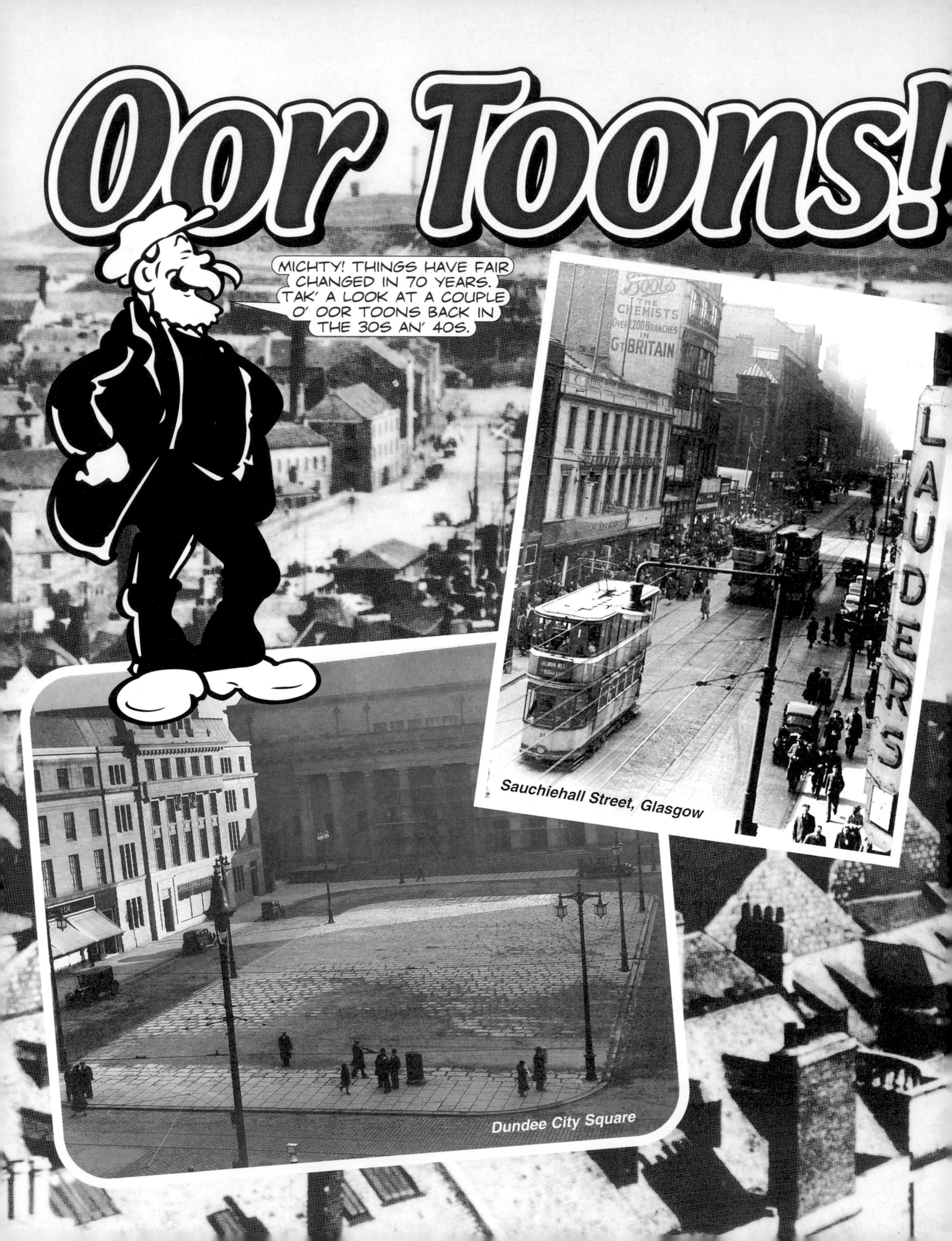
MICHTY! THINGS HAVE FAIR CHANGED IN 70 YEARS. TAK' A LOOK AT A COUPLE O' OOR TOONS BACK IN THE 30S AN' 40S.
Boots THE CHEMISTS OVER 1200 BRANCHES IN Gt BRITAIN
LAUDERS

Sauchiehall Street, Glasgow

Dundee City Square

Old City Hall, Perth

St Michael's Bridge, Dumfries

Princes Street, Edinburgh

Aberdeen Harbour

GIE'S AN EGG. I WANT TAE ROLL IT DOON THE WHINNEY DEN!
ANE LEFT, AN' IT'S AN AWFY JOB TAE GET EGGS—BUT YE CAN HAE IT! I'LL DYE IT AN' BOIL IT FOR THE MORN!
I'M AWA' TAE ROLL MA EGG!
JAMMY—WE'VE NAE EGGS—CAN I COME TAE?
WULLIE ARE AWA' TAE ROLL HIS EGG!
ER—WEEL
HA! HA! HA!
HO! HO! HO!
OH MY!

1941

I' BET THAE TWA ENGLISH LADS JOE AN' HEN ARE BRINGIN' THE NICHT WILL LIKE BEIN' AT A BURNS SUPPER!
AYE — WE'LL SHOW THEM A REAL SCOTCH NICHT!
THE HAGGIS LOOKS GRAND! SO DAE THE STOVIES AN' THE MEALY PUDDENS
RABBIE BURNS
16/6 !!!
WEE ERIC AND DUDLEY FROM LONDON, ARE COMIN'
THIS IS SAM ENTWHISTLE AN' THIS IS HARRY HAWKINS. THEY'VE BAITH BEEN LOOKIN' FORWARD TAE OUR BURNS SUPPER.
COME AWA' THEN, AN' WE'LL GET STARTED!
ERIC AN DUDLEY! — MEET THE BAIRN!
YOU MAY KISS MY 'HAUND!
NOW I'M TAE RECITE THE ADDRESS TO THE HAGGIS — "FAIR FA' YOUR HONEST SONSIE FACE, GREAT CHIEFTAIN O' THE PUDDIN'-RACE! ABOON THEM A' YE TAK YOUR PLACE —"
AN 'AGGIS? BLIMEY, WOT IS IT? DID YOU SHOOT IT OR DID IT DIE?
EE, BYGUM! IT'S SOME KIND OF FISH, AH RECKON
RABBIE BURNS
THIS 'ERE BURNS BLOKE IS O K., BUT YOU SHOULD 'EAR OUR WILLIAM SHAKESPEARE HE'S THE BEE'S-KNEES ENGLAND CAN SHOW YOU.
AWA' MAN. RABBIE BURNS HAS SHAKESPEARE LICKED A MILE
AYE LAAD. SHAKESPEARE WAS THE GREATEST POET
AM I HEARIN' RICHT!
WHIT!
DON'T BE SILLY!
RABBIE BURNS
SCOTLAND FOR EVER! WE BEAT YE AT BANNOCKBURN
OH, BUT WE WEREN'T TRYING THEN!
OH SIT DOON, JOE.
I'M GETTIN HYSTERICS
AWA' MAN! RANGERS COULD LICK BOLTON ONY DAY AN' WHIT ABOUT THE BLACK WATCH AN THE H.L.I. —
SHAKESPEARE FOR POETRY AND YORKSHIRE FOR CRICKET AN' BOLTON WANDERERS AN —
THIS IS AWFY, RABBIE — AN' ON YOUR NICHT TAE!
RABBIE BURNS
WHISTLE
HALF — TIME
WE GET PORRIDGE AN' KAIL AN PEASE BROSE IN SCOTLAND
AH, BUT WE GET ROAST BEEF AND APPLE TART, IN ENGLAND
NOW, NOW! DINNA FECHT ABOUT SCOTS AND ENGLISH. WE'RE ALL FRIENDS.
SO HERE'S A HAND MY TRUSTY FRIEN' AN' GIE'S A HAND O' THINE. THERE'LL ALWAYS BE AN ENGLAND — FOR THE SAKE O' AULD LANG SYNE!
WELL, YOU CAN'T BEAT SCOTLAND FOR 'OSPITALITY!
BOYS! HERE'S A TOAST THAT WID PLEASE RABBIE BURNS! "HERE'S TAE US! WHA'S LIKE US!"
RABBIE BURNS
ETERNAL FRIENDSHIP

The Sunday Post 26th January 1941

OOR WULLIE 1936-1946

HEY! WHIT ABOOT US GETTING UP A MOUTH ORGAN BAND AN' PRACTISIN' A BIT - THEN WE MICHT GET SAE GOOD WE COULD ENTERTAIN THE TROOPS!
HERE! THAT'S AN IDEA - LETS AWA' HAME AN GET OOR MOOTH ORGANS!
JINGS! IT'S AWFY CAULD PRACTISIN' IN HERE! I WISH WE HAD A WARM PLACE!
SHIVER
AYE!
NEXT DAY
SCHOOL
HULLO, MISTER JANITOR ARE YE BUSY?
AYE - I WISH YE COULD HELP ME WI' THE FIRES WULLIE.
OOH I LIKE DAEIN' THIS!
MY, YE'VE BEEN A GREAT HELP TAE ME WULLIE!
COULD I COME IN HERE THE MORN'S NICHT WHAUR IT'S WARM AN' PRACTISE MA MOOTH ORGAN BAND?
WEEL, THERE'S A CONCERT ON IN THE HALL, BUT YE CAN COME AN' HELP ME; THEN YE CAN PRACTISE EFTER
NEXT MORNING
THIS IS MR SCALES WHO IS GIVING THE CONCERT TONIGHT FOR CAPTAIN COX'S SOLDIERS SEE THAT THE HALL IS READY BY 7-30
AND I MUST HAVE THE PLACE PROPERLY CLEAN, TIDY, AND HEATED, MY MAN. NO MISTAKES NOW. DO YOU UNDERSTAND!
YES SIR!
THAT NIGHT
WAIL
SCRAPE
JINGS! WHIT A RACKET IN THE HALL!
AYE! THAT'S THAT NARKY BLOKE SCALES AN' HIS BAND
WE COULD DAE BETTER OORSEL'S!
HALF AN HOUR LATER.
THAE SOJERS MUST BE FED UP WI' THAT CHAMBER MUSIC - LET'S GIE 'EM THE TIGER RAG!
HA! HA! HA!
WISH ME LUCK WHEN YOU WAVE ME GOODBYE
COME ALONG! WE DIDN'T COME HERE TO BE LAUGHED AT.
I'LL HAVE TO SEE WHO CAUSED ALL THIS TROUBLE!
SO IT WAS YOU KIDS! WELL YOU'D BETTER COME IN AND CARRY ON WITH THE CONCERT!
LISTEN MEN - THIS IS OOR WULLIE AND HIS MOUTH ORGAN SWING BAND. THEY'LL CARRY ON.
ROLL OUT THE BARREL
CANTEEN
YOUSE LADS WIS THE GOODS
YE KNOCKED THAE SWANKY PLAYERS INTAE A COCKED HAT

The Sunday Post 9th February 1941

I'M GOIN' FOR SOME MESSAGES — DINNA YOU WAKEN YER PAW— HE'S TIRED!
SNOOZE
THAT'LL DAE FINE. LEAVE IT NOO!
MAW BACK AGAIN
HULLO, PAW! HAVE YE HAD A GUID SLEEP?
AN' WE DIDNA WAUKEN HIM, MAW!
OH-AUGH-AYE! YAWN
OH, MICHTY ME! I CANNA STRAIGHTEN MA BODY—WHIT'S GONE WRANG WI' ME?
OH DEAR! OH DEAR! THIS IS AWFY!
IS IT YER BACK, PAW?
NA' IT'S MA BODY! I'M TIED IN A KNOT I CANNA STAND STRAIGHT UP! OH, MICHTY!
AW! THIS IS TERRIBLE WHIT CAN IT BE?—JINGS I'LL SIGN THE PLEDGE THE MORN!
YE'LL NEED TAE GET TAE BED AT ONCE. I'LL GET THE DOCTOR.
HERE, I'LL BANDAGE YE UP, PAW!
WID IT BE MEASLES? NA! MEBBE STIFF NECK. HEY! WERE YE ON THE BASH LAST NICHT, PAW?
AW! MEBBE IT'S WHIT THEY CA' THE LUMBAGEY!
AUNT KATES HOME NURSING BOOK.
YE'D BETTER GET YER CLAES OFF AN' GET INTAE BED, PAW!
HUH! WHIT ARE YOU YINS LAUGHIN' AT—THIS IS'NA FUNNY! YER PUIR FAITHER'S MEBBE DYIN'!
AW LOOK! MA TIE'S PINNED TAE MA BREEKS!
ME A WEE COMIC! ME DID THAT!

The Sunday Post 2nd March 1941

I GOT THIS PICTURE TAE SELL TICKETS FOR THE RED CROSS!
BOOK OF TICKETS
PLEASE, WIFEY, BUY A 6D TICKET FOR THIS BONNY PICTER FOR THE RED CROSS
OH! YES GIVE ME FOUR
WHIT NICE! WE'LL TAK SIX TICKETS!
PLEASE, SIR, WILL YE BUY A TANNER TICKET FOR THIS PICTER, MR WATKINS.
DEAR ME! WHAT A HORRIBLE BIT OF WORK, BUT I'LL TAKE ONE CHANCE
AYE! THAT PICTER WAD HIDE THE MARK ON THE PARLOUR WA'. GIE'S SIX TICKETS, WULLIE.
3 HOURS LATER
NOO' I'LL COONT UP - THAT'S 38 HOOSES I'VE BEEN TAE, AN 93 TICKETS I'VE SELL'T. I'LL NEED TAE SELL 120 TAE GET £3 AN' I'M TIRED OOT TRAMPIN' ROOND WI' IT!
I KEN - I'LL SHOW IT ON THE PAVEMENT HERE AND GET MONEY FROM THE PASSERS BY.
SHOO!
SNIFF
GET AFF MA PICTER!
JINGS MIGHTY ME A FECHT!
ACH! THAT'S NAE USE! I'LL SHIFT FROM HERE!
CRASH!
CRIVVENS! LOOK AT MA PICTER — A' TYRE MARKS — AN' JINGS THERE'S CAT'S AN' DOG'S FEET MARKS ON IT TAE!
COME ON AN' HAE A GAME O' FITBA' WULLIE!
O.K.- ONLY FOR 5 MINUTES, THOUGH!
LET'S HAE A GAME OF "X AN' O'S"
FOOTBALL FINISHED
YE'LL NEED TAE HELP ME RAFFLE THIS PICTER!
JINGS! IT'S THE SAME ANE IS IT?
LOOK - THE FIRST TICKET TAE COME OOT O' THE HAT - Nº 37!
AW - THAT'S MR. WATKINS, THAT ARTIST BLOKE
YOU'VE WON THE PICTER MESTER WATKINS!
BAI JOVE! THAT'S WONDERFUL - HOW ARTY - REAL FUTURISTIC - HERE TAKE 5/- TO ADD TO YOUR FUND!

The Sunday Post 2nd March 1941

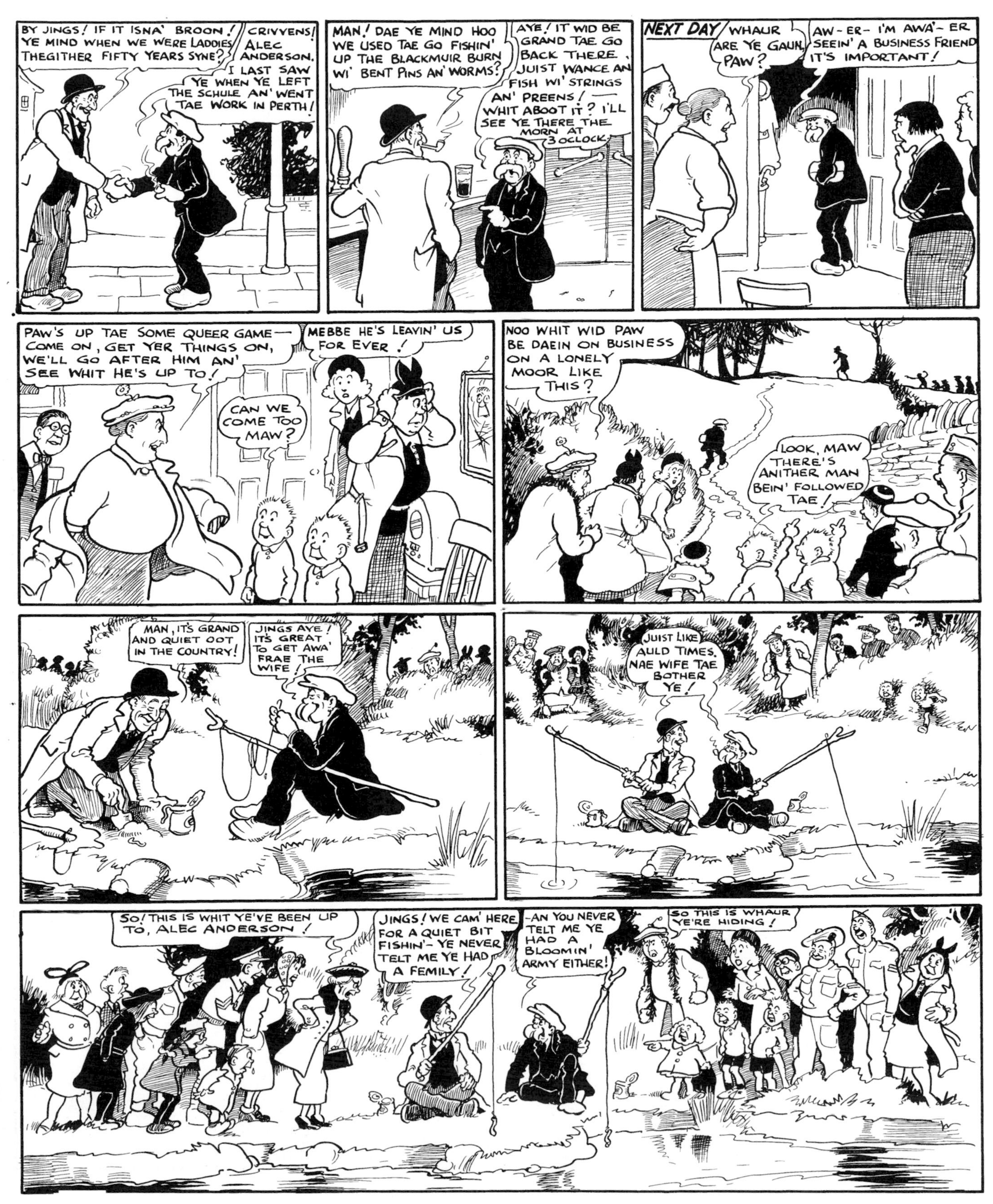
BY JINGS! IF IT ISNA' BROON! YE MIND WHEN WE WERE LADDIES THEGITHER FIFTY YEARS SYNE?
CRIVVENS! ALEC ANDERSON. I LAST SAW YE WHEN YE LEFT THE SCHULE AN' WENT TAE WORK IN PERTH!
MAN! DAE YE MIND HOO WE USED TAE GO FISHIN' UP THE BLACKMUIR BURN WI' BENT PINS AN' WORMS?
AYE! IT WID BE GRAND TAE GO BACK THERE, JUIST WANCE AN FISH WI' STRINGS AN' PREENS! — WHIT ABOOT IT? I'LL SEE YE THERE THE MORN AT 3 OCLOCK.
NEXT DAY
WHAUR ARE YE GAUN, PAW?
AW - ER - I'M AWA' - ER SEEIN' A BUSINESS FRIEND IT'S IMPORTANT!
PAW'S UP TAE SOME QUEER GAME — COME ON, GET YER THINGS ON, WE'LL GO AFTER HIM AN' SEE WHIT HE'S UP TO!
MEBBE HE'S LEAVIN' US FOR EVER!
CAN WE COME TOO MAW?
NOO WHIT WID PAW BE DAEIN ON BUSINESS ON A LONELY MOOR LIKE THIS?
LOOK, MAW THERE'S ANITHER MAN BEIN' FOLLOWED TAE!
MAN, IT'S GRAND AND QUIET OOT IN THE COUNTRY!
JINGS AYE! IT'S GREAT TO GET AWA' FRAE THE WIFE!
JUIST LIKE AULD TIMES. NAE WIFE TAE BOTHER YE!
SO! THIS IS WHIT YE'VE BEEN UP TO, ALEC ANDERSON!
JINGS! WE CAM' HERE FOR A QUIET BIT FISHIN' - YE NEVER TELT ME YE HAD A FEMILY!
-AN YOU NEVER TELT ME YE HAD A BLOOMIN' ARMY EITHER!
SO THIS IS WHAUR YE'RE HIDING!

The Sunday Post 15th June 1941

OOR WULLIE 1936-1946

MAW-GIE'S AN EGG. I WANT TAE ROLL IT DOON THE WHINNEY DEN!
WEEL, THERE'S ONLY ANE LEFT, AN' IT'S AN AWFY JOB TAE GET EGGS — BUT YE CAN HAE IT! I'LL DYE IT AN' BOIL IT FOR THE MORN!
NEXT DAY
HULLO, SOAPY. I'M AWA' TAE ROLL MA EGG!
YOU'RE JAMMY— WE'VE NAE EGGS—CAN I COME TAE?
HULLO, BOB, ME AN' WULLIE ARE AWA' TAE ROLL HIS EGG!
JINGS! I WISH I HAD AN EGG— CAN I COME WI' YE?
ER—WEEL— O.K.
THERE'S THE WHINNEY DEN-WE'LL ROLL IT THERE!
WE'LL ROLL IT DOON HERE, SYNE I'LL EAT IT!
AW, BUT WE SHOULD GET A BITTIE!
WHA'S EGG IS IT ONYWEY?
WEEL, BE FAIR, WE SHOULD DRAW LOTS FOR IT, OR RAFFLE IT!
AYE!
NA! WE'LL ROLL IT AN' THEN RACE FOR IT—! WHA GETS IT FIRST EATS IT!
O.K. THEN!
HAUF A MEENIT THEN, TILL I GET A STICK!
WHIT'S THE STICK FOR?
TAE HELP ME TAE RUN QUICKER—! READY—GO!
WE'VE LEFT WULLIE BEHIND!
TRIP
JINGS! IT WIS WULLIE THAT TRIPPED ME UP—!
TRIP
THAT WISNA' FAIR! YE TRIPPED US!
ACH! IT WIS AN ACCIDENT! I'M AFF TAE EAT MA EGG!
AW GEE!
NOO FOR A FEED!
PHEW!
ROTTEN
AW GEE, LADS— I'M SORRY I DIDNA' PLAY FAIR! I'LL GIE YE A HAUF EACH. I DINNA' DESERVE ONY AT A'—! OPEN YER MOOTHS AN' SHUT YER EEN!
BUT EFTER A', WULLIE, IT WIS YOUR EGG!
THIS IS AWFY GUID O' YE, WULLIE—!
BL-L-AR!
JINGS! IT'S POISON!

The Sunday Post 13th April 1941

IT'S GRAND TAE HAE OBLIGIN' FRIENDS WHA'LL GIE YE A LEN' O' THEIR BIKES!
AYE, WE CAN A' HAE A RIN THEGITHER!
HUH! NAE FAIRY CYCLES FOR ME- I'M ON A REAL MAN'S BIKE!
LATER
JINGS! YOU'LL NO GET SADDLE SAIR ON YOUR BIKE. ONYWEY- 'COS YE CANNA REACH THE SADDLE!
WHIT! YE'RE TRYIN' TAE TELL ME I'M NO BIG ENOUGH FOR A MAN'S BIKE EH? - AWA! YOU AN' YER CISSY FAIRY CYCLES!
COME ON, YOU YINS! I'VE GOT THE SAN'WICHES AN' TEA READY!
WE GANG RICHT UP THE ROAD THERE - IT'S ONLY A THIRD CLASS ANE ON THE MAP BUT IT TAK'S YE TAE THE MAIN ROAD EFTER THREE MILES OR SO!
AYE!
ON THE 'ROAD' AGAIN
IT'S A THIRD CLASS ROAD A' RICHT!
AW! BUT IT GETS BETTER FURTHER ON— AW JINGS! WHIT A HOLE!
CRIVVENS! THIS IS AWFY- I'M BEIN' SHAKEN LIKE AN ASH PAN LEAF!
BUMP
JINGS! THE ROAD'S JUIST RIN RICHT INTAE THE HEATHER! I THOCHT YE SAID WE'D GET TAE THE MAIN ROAD THIS WEY, PAW!
AW! IT'LL BE THE MAP THAT'S WRANG - WE'LL JUIST NEED TAE GANG BACK THE WEY WE CAM'!
HUH! MAP'S WRANG, EH! I KEN WHA'S WRANG!
ARE WE AT THE MAIN ROAD YET.
JINGS! I'M TIRED!
SO THIS IS THE MAIN ROAD. A' I CAN SEE IS A GOAT TRACK UP THE MOUNTAINSIDE — AN IT'S GETTIN' DARK!
AN HOUR LATER
WEEL, WE'RE ON THE MAIN ROAD AT LAST!
WE CANNA RIDE OOR BIKES- IT'S PAST LIGHTIN' UP TIME AN' WE'VE NAE LAMPS!
LET'S ASK A LORRY TAE GIE'S A HURL!
AYE! YOU VAMP THE LORRY DRIVER DAPHNE. THEN HE'LL GIE THE FAMILY A LIFT!
NA! NA! I'M NO' GLAMOROUS THE NICHT!
DAE YE WANT A LIFT INTAE THE TOON? — JUIST SHOVE YER BIKES ON THE LORRY!
JINGS! I'M GLAD O' THIS!
AW, THANKS JOCK, THE WIFE AN' THE WEANS ARE FAIR FAGGIT!
HOME AGAIN
QUICK PAW AN' OPEN THE DOOR AND LET'S GET IN, IT WIS GEY CAULD ON THE BACK O' THON LORRY!
IT WIS AWFY GUID O' THE DRIVER TAE TAK A' US LOT- HE WIS A RARE FELLA!
MIND YE DINNA TURN ON ONY LIGHTS TILL WE'VE GOT THE BLACK OUT FIXED!
THE BIKES ARE SAFE IN THE WASHIN' HOOSE, MAW!
OH! WEE LAMB'S TIRED!
WHIT A PLESTER IT IS GETTIN' THE BLACK OUTS UP IN THE DARK. NOW I'LL SWITCH THE LIGHT ON!
HAR! HAR! HAR! LOOK AT YOUR FACE!
MICHTY ME! WE'RE A' BLACK!
AW JINGS! I DIDNA KEN THON WIS A COAL LORRY!
HUH! LOOK AT YOURS!
CRIVVENS! MA GLAMOUR'S A' GONE!

The Sunday Post 7th September 1941

OOR WULLIE 1936-1946

WICKET
HOORAY! WULLIE'S OOT!
COME ON, WULLIE! GIE'S THE BAT. IT'S MY SHOT NOO!
OCH AWA - I'M NO OOT - I WISNA LOOKIN' ONYWEY IT'S NO' YOUR BAT - IT'S MINE'S!
I KEN WHIT I'LL DAE!
LOOK! YE CAN SEE WHAUR THE BALL HIT SLAP ON THE MIDDLE STUMP!
CREAK
CRACK
AW! YE ROTTER!
WAIT TILL WE GET YE!
BACK HOME
WULLIE, I'VE GOT YOU A NEW SUIT - FOR SUNDAYS TRY IT ON AN' LET'S SEE HOW YE LOOK IN IT!
AW, BUT MAW! I LIKE MA DUNGAREES BEST!
THERE NOW! YE LOOK AWFY SMAIRT IN IT!
CRIVVENS! THERE'S FAT BOB AN' THEM WAITIN' OOTSIDE TAE GET ME!
THOUGHT
NOW IF I GANG OOT WI' MA NEW SUIT ON, THEY'LL NO TOUCH ME!
OH, MAW! WHIT ABOOT ME GAUN TAE SEE AUNTIE ANNIE WI' MA NEW SUIT ON?
THAT WID BE RARE - SHE'D BE AWFY PLEASED TAE SEE YE!
YE CANNA BELT ME NOO WI' THIS NEW SUIT ON LADS!
FOOLED AGAIN!
THIS IS MA AUNTIE'S HOUSE - AN' I BET YE I GET A GRAUND TEA - YE CAN WATCH ME THROUGH THE WINDIE - TAE PROVE IT!
KNOCK
WAIT TILL WE GET YE IN YER DUNGAREES AGAIN!
G-R-R
RASP
I TELT YE!
COME ON LADS I'VE AN IDEA TAE MAK' WULLIE FECHT!
AND HERE'S A SHILLING TO PUT IN YOUR POCKET!
AW GEE THANKS AUNTIE - YE'RE AWFY KIND!
CRIVVENS! A SHULL'N TAE! - BUT JUIST YOU WAIT!
YE DIDNA KEN I WIS AN ARTIST, WULLIE!
WULLIE IS A SAFTIE (SINED - FAT BOB)
Wullie is a fool and a donkey at the school.
RAGE
Wullie is a Pansy He is feored to fecht!
(SIGNED - SOAPY SOUTAR)
CALL ME A SAFTY AN' A PANSY WID YE? COME ON - NEW SUIT OR NO NEW SUIT! I'LL BASH YE!
HUH! I'LL FECHT BAITH THE THREE O' YE!
THAT'S SPOILT MA NEW SUIT - AN' I'VE GOT A BLACK EYE - A THICK EAR AN A JEELYNOSE - BUT THEY'VE GOT THREE BLACK EEN - TWA THICK EARS - AN FOUR OR FIVE JEELY NOSES!
Z-Z-Z

The Sunday Post 20th July 1941

OH DEAR! I MET THAT GOSSIPIN' AULD FAGGOT LIZZIE TAMSON. SHE SAYS SHE'LL BE COMIN' ROOND THE NICHT! SHE WIS GONE AFORE I COULD SAY NO!
OH, THE BELLS WERE TELLIN' ME THEY WID BE VISITIN' US THIS WEEK - AN' IT'S NEAR THE END O' THE WEEK NOO!
THAT'S FUNNY! I HEARD THE ANDERSONS WERE COMIN' TAE!
I CANNA STAND THAE FOWK! THEY'LL COME AN' GOSSIP AN' SPILE THE HALE NICHT. I WINNA HAE IT! I'D RAITHER GANG OOT!
JINGS! THAE AULD CRAWS!
DANDY
KNOCK
KNOCK
WHISPER—THAT'LL BE SOME O' THEM NOO—SHALL I GO TAE THE DOOR?
SSH — NA! NA! KEEP QUIET — AN' THEY'LL THINK WE'RE NO' IN!
SH-SH!
SH-SH
FUNNY, THEY MUST BE OOT! AN' I SAID WE'D BE OWER TAE SEE THEM!
COME ON, LET'S AWA' MAW!
THE BELLS
SH-SH! IT IS THE BELLS — AN' THEY'RE GAEIN' AWA'!
LATER
LIZZIE TAMSON
KNOCK
KNOCK
SH-SH
WHA IS IT NOO?
I'M NO' IN!
OCH! IT'S NAE USE STANDIN' THERE KNOCKIN' A' NICHT! THEY'RE NO' IN!
THAT WIS LIZZIE TAMSON A' RICHT! HERE— LET'S A' GANG ACROSS TAE SANDY LOW'S HOOSE! SANDY'S IS AYE A CHEERY PLACE!
AYE, LET'S GO AFORE THE ANDERSONS GET HERE!
QUICK! THAT SOUNDS LIKE THEM ON THE STAIRS NOO! LET'S HIDE UP THE STAIR TILL THEY GO!
CLOMP
CLOMP
FOOTSTEPS
COME AWA', YOU BAIRNS!
TIP-TOE
SH-SH
I CANNA MAK' ONYBODY HEAR. THEY MUST BE OOT!
AW! LET'S AWA'! IT'S NAE USE KNOCKIN'!
HAMMER
THE ANDERSONS
AT SANDY LOW'S
QUICK, SANDY! LET'S IN. WE'VE COME OWER FOR A QUIET EVENIN'. WE'RE DODGIN' VISITORS.
WELL, WE DODGED THEM A' RICHT!
OH, ARE YE — WE'LL COME IN AND SEE THIS—
CRIVVENS!
YOU YINS!
—AN' AS I WIS SAYIN'— YE'LL MEBBE NO BELIEVE ME — BUT THON MRS —
I DINNA KEN HOO OFTEN HER MAN GETS CLEAN UNDERCLAES— FOR THERE'S NEVER ONY ON THE CLAES LINE— I KEN, BECAUSE I'VE WATCHED!
HERE— BUT WAIT TILL I TELL YE—!
ME FEEL SICK!

The Sunday Post 28th September 1941

Gettin' Aboot

A CAR'S NEARLY AS GUID AS A CARTIE.
YL 4117
TRAMS WERE RICHT BRAW F'R GETTIN' YE INTAE TOON.

1930s Bentley

Single deck tram

Ye cannae beat a good cartie but they had some braw ways o' gettin' aboot back in thae days. The auld steam trains an' trams and auld cars... whit braw.

BUT FOR LANG HURLS YE CANNAE WHACK A STEAM TRAIN.
CRASH
UNLESS YE WANT TAE FLY. MICHTY. I'D FAIR LOVE TAE HAVE FLOWN IN ONE O' THAE BOMBERS.

The Flying Scotsman

De Haviland

DID YE GET THAT THICK EAR?
HE'S GOT AN AWFY TEMPER!
HULLO MISTER PENTER! CAN I WATCH YE PENT?
ONYTHING! I'LL NEED TAE GO BACK FOR MA STEPS!
DINNA LET ONYBODY TOUCH IT – I'LL NO' BE LANG!
O.K. MISTER! LEAVE IT TAE ME!
WANG
JINGS! THANKS!

1942

—WELL, I'M A HEALTH SPECIALIST, AND I OUGHT TO KNOW — IF YOU DO THESE THINGS YOU WILL NEVER HAVE A COLD OR A COUGH ALL THE WINTER — GARGLE EVERY DAY — USE A DISINFECTANT IN YOUR ROOMS—DRINK A GOOD TONIC — ALWAYS SLEEP WITH YOUR WINDOWS OPEN AND YOU'LL BE O.K.!
WEEL, THAT SOUNDS HEALTHY!
WE'LL NEED TAE TRY IT MAW!
(ASIDE) ACH! HE'S A HAVERIN' GOAT!
THAT NIGHT
COME ON, NOO — WE'RE A' TAE GARGLE WIR THROATS — NAE COLDS OR COUGHS — THIS WINTER!
GOGGLE! GOGGLE
YOU'LL BETTER GARGLE TAE OR YOU'LL GET LAID OOT WI' THE FLU'!
NA! NA! NAE NEW-FANGLED IDEAS FOR ME!
HEY! YE'RE DAEIN' IT THE WRANG WAY!
JINGS! THIS HAS AN AWFY TASTE!
CRIVVENS! I'VE SWOLLOWED IT — UGH!
NEXT NIGHT
THIS IS A REAL STRONG MIXTURE! WE'LL SPRAY THE HOOSE AN' KILL A' THE FLU' GERMS!
OOH! WHIT A STINK!
IT NIPS YER E'EN!
STILL, IT'S WORTH IT, NO TAE HAE A COLD! BREATHE IT IN!
AW MAW! IT'S MAKIN' ME GREET!
COUGH
MICHTY ME! WHIT DAFT STUNT'S THIS?
NEXT NIGHT
"THIS SPECIAL EXTRACT IS FULL OF VITAMINS"— IT SAYS SO ON THE BOTTLE! COME ON NOO!
UGH! IT'S TERRIBLE!
BLA-A-AH! YOU'RE TELLIN' ME—BUT— GR-OO-OH IT'LL KEEP AWA' THE FLU'!
I'M NO' FOR ONY O' THAE FANCY TONICS!
WHIT'S IT LIKE?
IT'S A KIND O' STORMY SLEEPIN' WI' THE WINDIES OPEN—!
AW - THERE'S THE BED CLAES AWA'!
BLAST
HOWL
ARE YE A' NICE AN' COSY?
NEXT DAY AT GRAN' PAW'S
HERE'S A NOTE FRAE THE BROONS IN GLEBE STREET!
Dear Granpaw Come over at once. we're in a terrible fix Ma
YE LOT O' DAFT GOWKS - YE'VE A' GOT THE FLU' EFTER A' — BUT IT A' COMES BACK ON ME – I'VE GOT TAE LOOK EFTER YE!
GRAN' PAW! I WANT A HOT-WATER BOTTLE!
GRAN' PAW! THERE'S NAE SUGAR IN MA TEA!
GRAN' PAW! BRING SOME HANKIES!

The Sunday Post 11th January 1942

LOOK WULLIE - IT'S A STRAY CAT I FOUND IN THE STREET, SO I'M LOOKIN' EFTER IT!
OCH! IT'S ONLY A CAT! HOO CAN YE NO' LOOK EFTER SOMETHING WORTH WHILE?
LATER
JINGS! A STRAY BULL-DOG! HE LOOKS LOST! HERE BOY! HERE DOGGIE!
I'LL HAE TAE LET FAT BOB SEE THIS ANE! IT'S A SIGHT BETTER THAN A STRAY CAT! COME ON IN TAE MA SHED, DOGGIE!
Wullie's Shed
WHIT DAE YE THINK O' THE BONNY DOG I'VE FOUND? I KIN HANDLE HIM A' RICHT. I'LL JUIST TIE THIS STRING ON HIM AN' WE'LL TAK HIM HAME!
HE LOOKS AN AWFY FIERCE BRUTE!
HURRY UP AN' PIT THAT STRING ON HIM WULLIE - I WANT TAE GANG HAME!
FINE DOGGIE! I'M TAKIN' YE FOR A WALK!
GROWL
HALF AN HOUR LATER
THIS IS AWFY, WULLIE HE'LL NO' LET US NEAR HIM - AN' I CANNA GET PAST THE DOOR AN' MA DENNER'S READY!
MAYBE WE CAN GET HIM IN THIS SACK, COME ON BOY!
WEEL, THAT'S GOT HIM NOO I'LL TAK' HIM TAE HIS HAME!
-AN' I CAN GET HAME TAE. CHEERIO, WULLIE!
BARK
YELP
CRIVVENS! I'VE FORGOTTEN TAE LOOK AT THE ADDRESS ON IT'S COLLAR I'LL HAE TAE OPEN THE SACK AGAIN!
ROAR
BARK
G-RRR
HELP!
JINGS! HE'S EFTER ME!
HELP! HE'S PULLIN' MA BREEKS AFF!
AW JINGS, COME HERE WI' MY DUNGAREES!
WINTER COM'S
ACH! HE'S BACK TAE THE SAME PLACE WHERE I FIRST FOUND HIM COME ON DOGGIE! GIE WULLIE HIS BREEKS BACK! NICE DOG! NICE DOG!
NICE DOG! YE BRUTE — NICE BRUTE!
TAK' THAT! I SAW YE TRYIN' TAE STEAL PADDY THE DAY, BUT I KENT HE'D COME BACK!
BUT I DIDNA' KEN YER DOG LIVED HERE!

The Sunday Post 15th February 1942

HULLO, MRS BROON! I WONDER IF YE'D MIND TAKIN' CARE O' JOCKIE, MA CANARY — I'M GAEIN' AWA' FOR A WEEK!

WHY, OF COURSE, MRS THOMSON, WE'D LOVE TAE HAVE HIM — HE'LL BE A' RICHT WI' US!

3 DAYS LATER

WE'VE HAD HIM IN THE CAGE FOR THREE DAYS NOO. MEBBE WE'D BETTER LET HIM OOT FOR A BIT EXERCISE!

AYE, IT'LL DO HIM GOOD!

THESE ROUTE MARCHES ARE AWFY EH!

AYE, I'M BROWNED OFF!

THERE! HE'S FREE! LET'S SEE WHIT HE DOES!

AW JINGS! HE'S FLOWN RICHT INTO THE JAM RATION!

HE'LL BE A' STICKY!

LET'S GIE HIM A BATH!

RASPBERRY JAM

COME ON NOO, JOCKIE—DINNA BE FEART—HAE A BATH!

BE CAREFUL NOW!

NICE JOCKIE!

I'LL USE MA WATER-PISTOL ON IT!

WHIZZ

JINGS, WHIT A FLEG!

OH DEAR LOOK WHIT YE'VE DONE!

GOT IT—NO—MISSED! SORRY, PAW!

LOOK, HE'S LANDED ON MA HEID—LET THE BAIRN TAK HIM OFF—HE'LL NO BE SCARED O' HER!

NO, LEAVE HIM!

OH, JINGS! HE'S AWA' AGAIN!

THEY'RE MAKIN' AN AWFY ROW — THEY'LL BE HAEIN' FUN WI' JOCKIE MAYBE WE SHOULD HAE LEFT HIM WI' THEM FOR THE WEEK EVEN THOUGH WE'VE COME HAME SOONER THAN WE THOCHT!

AYE, THEY'LL BE SORRY TAE LOSE HIM!

RACKET YELL

BROWN

LOOK AT HIM! EFTER US TRYIN' TAE BATH HIM—HE WASHES HIMSEL'!

The Sunday Post 15th March 1942

OOR WULLIE 1936-1946

JINGS! I'LL BE LATE FOR THE SCHOOL - THAT'S WI' STAYIN' OOT LATE AT THE PICTERS LAST NICHT! I'VE SLEPT IN!
WATCH
WILLIAM, YOU'RE A QUARTER OF AN HOUR LATE! HOLD OUT YOUR HAND!
'EARLY TO BED, EARLY TO RISE' SHOULD BE YOUR MOTTO! GET UP EARLY IN THE MORNING - TAKE SOME HEALTHY EXERCISE AND THEN GET TO SCHOOL EARLY!
THAT NIGHT
WEEL, I'M NO' GETTIN' THE STRAP THE MORN FOR BEIN' LATE! I'LL GET TAE MA BED NOW AN' BE AT THE SCHOOL AFORE ONYBODY!
I'LL SET THE ALARM TAE GO AFF AT FIVE O'CLOCK! THAT'LL GET ME UP NICE AN' EARLY!
INTAE BED AT HAUF PAST ECHT! - I'LL GET A RARE LANG SLEEP!
LATER
JINGS! IT'S TWENTY PAST NINE AN' I HAVENA' GOT TAE SLEEP YET!
MUCH LATER
CRIVVENS! IT'S ELEVEN O'BLINKIN' CLOCK! AN' I'M NO' ASLEEP YET! THIS IS WHIT YE GET FOR GOIN' TAE BED EARLY! I WISNA' TIRED ENOUGH TAE SLEEP!
5 O'CLOCK NEXT MORNING
BR-RRR-R
JINGS! I MUST HAE BEEN SLEEPIN' - IT'S 5 O'CLOCK A'READY! WHIT A SHORT NICHT! CRIVVEN'S! IT'S CAULD!
WHIT'LL I DAE TILL BREAKFAST TIME? I KEN - I'LL DAE WHIT TEACHER SAID AN' TAK' SOME EXERCISE!
I'LL RUN FOR THREE MILES. I DINNA HAE SHORTS SO I'LL WEAR PAW'S PANTS!
THAT WIS A GOOD FIVE MILES I RAN - OR WIS IT FOWER? MAYBE IT WIS THREE? WEEL IT WIS TWA ONYWAY, OR ANE AN A HAUF!
WULLIE'S HOOSE
MY! IT'S ONLY SEVEN O'CLOCK YET! I WISH MAW WID GET UP AN' MAK' MA BREAKFAST!
SHIVER
LATER
JINGS! I FEEL A KIND O' SLEEPY NOW I'VE HAD MA BREAKFAST! STILL I'LL BE EARLY AT THE SCHOOL IT'S ONLY EIGHT O'CLOCK!
I WISH THE JANITOR WID COME AN' OPEN THE GATES! IT'S CAULD SITTIN' HERE!
BOYS' SCHOOL
MY! YOU'RE THE FIRST LADDIE TAE GET TAE SCHOOL THIS MORNIN'! WHIT'S WRANG?
BOYS' SCHOOL
I'M JUIST DAEIN' IT TAE PLEASE TEACHER!
MY GOODNESS, WILLIAM! I'M GLAD TO SEE YOU IN SCHOOL SO EARLY!
PRIDE
NOW BOYS, NONE OF YOU WERE VERY EARLY FOR SCHOOL THIS MORNING, EXCEPT WILLIAM - HE WAS HERE FIRST! HIS MOTTO IS 'EARLY TO BED, EARLY TO RISE'!
TIRED
HALF AN HOUR LATER
WILLIAM! HOW DARE YOU SLEEP IN CLASS! COME OUT HERE! SOUTAR - WAKE HIM UP!
SNORE!
SNORT!
COMING IN LATE FOR SCHOOL IS BAD ENOUGH, BUT SNORING IN CLASS IS WORSE!
WHIT'S THE USE!

The Sunday Post 15th November 1942

I'M GOIN' WI' YE TAE THE TRAVEL LECTURE BY LORD AND LADY SMYTHE THE MORN'S NICHT IN THE MISSION HALL. WHAT ARE YE TAE WEAR AT IT?
OCH! I'M JUIST GAUN IN MA FEATHER BOA! AN' PAW WILL WEAR HIS BONNET!
BUT JINGS! YE CANNA GO LIKE THAT! WHIT WID LORD AN' LADY SMYTHE THINK O' FOLK TURNIN' UP LIKE A COUPLE O' TINKS?
WHIT'S THAT? I CANNA' HEAR RICHT. I'VE GOT WAX IN MA EARS!
BUT MAW-!
MA FEATHER BOA'S FINE!
YE'RE TAE WEAR YER BOWLER HAT!
NA, I'LL NO!
GRAN'PAW'S DEAF-YE CAN SAY ONYTHING TAE HIM, HE'LL NO' HEAR YE! TELL HIM HE'S A DAFT AULD GOWK!
HEY! YE STUPID LOOKIN' AULD GOAT! AWA' AN GET YER LUGS CLEANED OOT!
WHIT'S THAT YE'RE SAYIN', MA WEE LAMBS?
NEXT DAY
I'VE WRAPPED MAW'S FEATHER BOA AN' PAW'S BONNET IN A PIECE O' PAPER AN' HID THEM UP THE CHIMNEY! THEY'LL NEVER FIND THEM THERE
S-SSH! HERE'S GRAN'PAW!
OCH! YE NEEDNA' BOTHER ABOOT THON SILLY AULD FAGGOT, HE'S DEAF!
HULLO!
IT'S NEARLY TIME FOR THE MEETIN' AN' I CANNA FIND MA FEATHER BOA ONY PLACE!
HAE YOU BEEN PLAYIN' WI' MA BONNET! WHAUR IS IT?
DINNA WORRY, YOU TWA! I KEN WHAUR THEY ARE!
CRIVVENS! JINGS! HOO DID GRAN'PAW KEN THE HIDIN' PLACE?
VEIL
OH, I KENT A' RICHT! CA' ME A SILLY AULD FAGGOT, WID YE?-WHEN YE THOCHT I WIS DEAF-BUT I'D JUIST HAD MA EARS CLEANED OOT AN I HEARD YE SAY YE'D HIDE THE THINGS UP THE CHIMNEY! HA! HA!
HUH! SO YOU ANES HID MA FEATHER BOA, DID YE?
BUT MAW, YE LOOK SIC A SICHT IN IT!
WHIT'S WRANG WI' ME IN A BONNET ONYWAY!
CRIVVENS! WHEN YE'RE GOIN' TAE HEAR A REAL LORD AN' A LADY - IT'S A BOWLER HAT OR NOTHING!
DINNA PAY ONY 'TENTION!
LOOK! I'M NO' THE ONLY ANE WI' A FEATHER BOA! SHE'S GOT ANE TAE!
THAT'S NAE EXCUSE FOR YOU! THE SMYTHES WILL STILL THINK YE'RE ORRY!
I AM PLEASED TO INTRODUCE LORD AND LADY SMYTHE, WHO ARE TO TELL US TO-NIGHT ABOUT THEIR TRAVELS IN AFRICA-!
MY GOODNESS! IT'S THE WIFIE WI' THE FEATHER BOA! LADY SMYTHE!
CRIVVENS! THE AULD LAD IS LORD SMYTHE-WI' A BONNET LIKE MINE!
HAW! HAW!

The Sunday Post 8th November 1942

OOR WULLIE 1936-1946

WHAUR DID YE GET THAT THICK EAR?
MA FAITHER GAVE IT ME THIS MORNIN' FOR BEIN' IMPIDENT! HE'S GOT AN AWFY TEMPER!
LATER
HULLO MISTER PENTER! CAN I WATCH YE PENT?
AYE, IF YE DINNA TOUCH ONYTHING! I'LL NEED TAE GO BACK FOR MA STEPS!
YOU WATCH MA BARROW. DINNA LET ONYBODY TOUCH IT – I'LL NO' BE LANG!
O.K. MISTER! LEAVE IT TAE ME!
15 MINUTES LATER
THE PENTER'S AN AWFY LANG TIME COMIN' BACK!
HALF AN HOUR PASSES
I'LL TAK' A SHORT CUT THROUGH HERE!
I'LL AWA' AN' LOOK FOR HIM!
JINGS! I WONDER WHAUR HE IS!
CRIVVENS – WHAUR'S THE LADDIE AN' THE BARROW!
I'LL AWA' AN' FIND HIM! MAYBE HE'S GONE THIS WAY!
HAE YE SEEN A WEE LADDIE PUSHIN' A PAINTER'S BARROW? THE WEE RASCAL! I LEFT HIM TAE LOOK AFTER IT – AN' HE'S TA'EN IT AWA'!
OH?
IT'S NAE USE! I CANNA FIND THE PENTER – I'LL AWA' BACK AN' SEE IF HE'S THERE!
HA! IS THAT PENT YE'VE GOT THERE? LET'S SEE IT!
IF YE TOUCH THIS I'LL GET MA FAITHER TAE GIE YE ANITHER THICK EAR!
WHIT'S THIS? – RED PENT!
LEAVE IT ALANE! IT'S – ER – MA FAITHER'S PENT!
OUCH!
RED
YE WEE SPITFIRE! TAK' THAT!
I'LL TELL MA FAITHER ON YOU!
HUH! I'M NO' FEART O' YOUR FAITHER – MY FAITHER COULD KNOCK YOUR'S SILLY!
HAUD STILL – I'M PENTIN' YELLOW SPOTS ON YER DUNGAREES!
YELLOW
NOW I'LL PENT YER FAITHER'S BARROW A' THE COLOURS O' THE RAINBOW!
YE ROTTER! JUIST YOU WAIT!
HAE YE SEEN A PENTER LOOKIN' FOR HIS BARROW?
I'LL SAY I DID, WULLIE! AN' HE'S RAGIN' MAD!
OH JINGS! I'M IN FOR IT NOO!! AN' I'M SCARED STIFF BUT I'LL AWA' AN TELL THE PENTER WHAUR HIS BARROW IS—
P-PLEASE – I COULDNA' HELP IT – A BIG LAD SET ON ME! LOOK WHIT HE'S DONE TAE ME!
YE'D NAE BUSINESS MOVIN' MA BARROW! WHAUR IS IT NOO?
COME ON AN' I'LL SHOW YE!
THERE YE ARE!
SO! I GAVE YE A SKELP IN THE EAR THIS MORNIN' AN' THIS IS HOO YE GET YER AIN BACK!
BUT PAW! I DIDNA KEN THIS WIS YOUR BARROW! THAT WEE LAD SAID IT WIS HIS FAITHER'S!
OH YEAH! YE SHOULD'VE KENT IT WIS MA BARROW – SO THERE'S ANITHER THICK EAR TAE YE!
WANG
JINGS!
YE'RE A BRAVE LADDIE – STANDIN' UP TAE THIS WILD LAD O' MINE! HERE'S TWA BOB TAE TAK' THE PENT AFF!
HOWL
JINGS! THANKS!
THE PENT CAN STAY ON! I'LL KEEP THE TWA BOB!

The Sunday Post 6th December 1942

OCH! THE ENGLISH ARE NO' SAE BAD!
1943
HULLO, WULLIE, WILL YE HAUD MA PIG UNTIL I GET SOME BACCY?—I'M JUIST AWA' TAE MARKET TAE SELL IT, I'LL LIKELY GET £10 FOR IT!
TOBACCONIST
LOOK! I'LL GIE YE A SHOT AT PULLIN' ME IN MA BARROW, PIGGIE!
RIGHT! IT'S A DEAL!
WALLACE
I'VE SELL'T IT!
£12-10— AN' NAE BOTHER!!

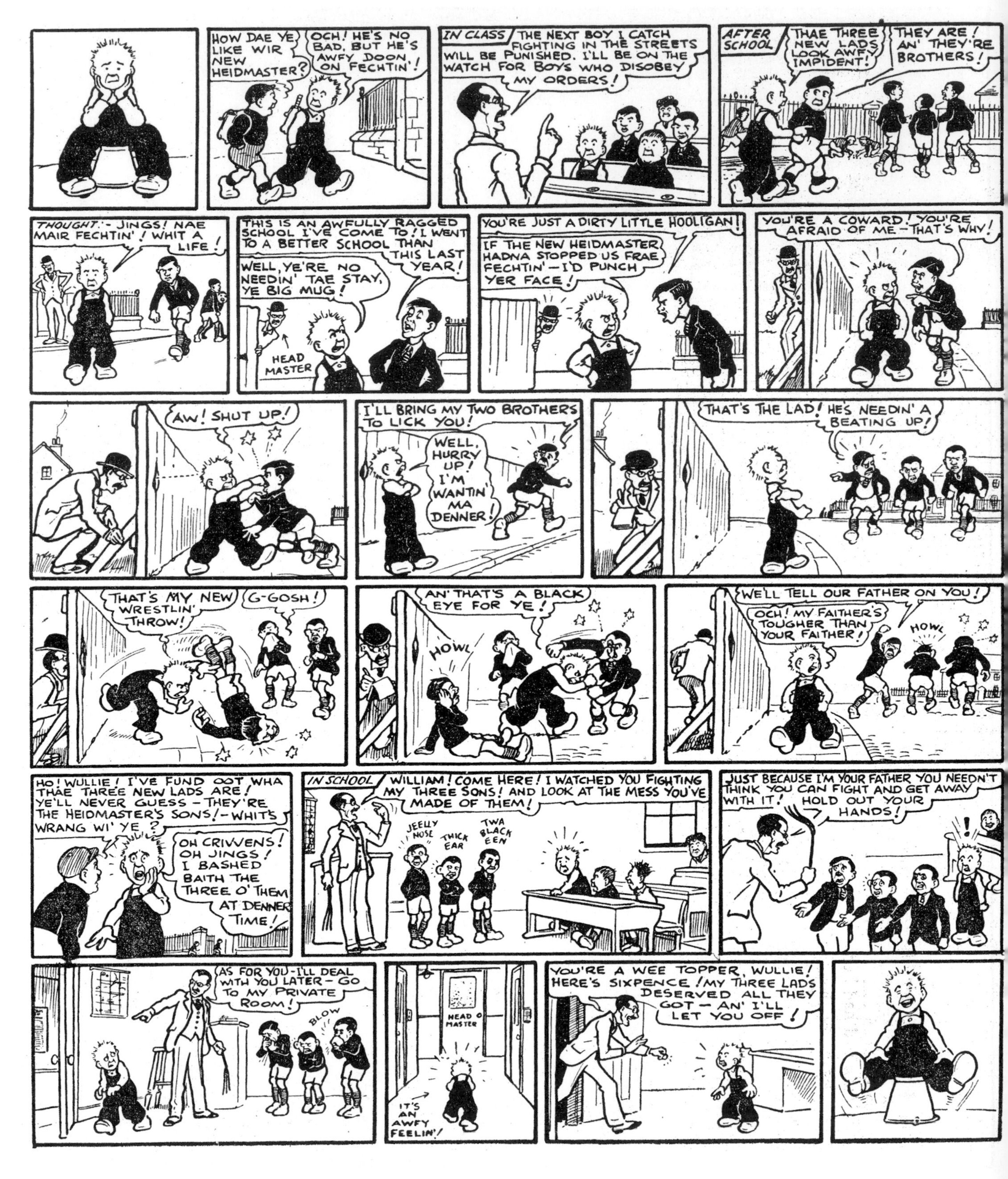
HOW DAE YE LIKE WIR NEW HEIDMASTER?
OCH! HE'S NO BAD, BUT HE'S AWFY DOON ON FECHTIN'!
IN CLASS
THE NEXT BOY I CATCH FIGHTING IN THE STREETS WILL BE PUNISHED. I'LL BE ON THE WATCH FOR BOYS WHO DISOBEY MY ORDERS!
AFTER SCHOOL
THAE THREE NEW LADS LOOK AWFY IMPIDENT!
THEY ARE! AN' THEY'RE BROTHERS!
THOUGHT:- JINGS! NAE MAIR FECHTIN'! WHIT A LIFE!
THIS IS AN AWFULLY RAGGED SCHOOL I'VE COME TO! I WENT TO A BETTER SCHOOL THAN THIS LAST YEAR!
WELL, YE'RE NO NEEDIN' TAE STAY, YE BIG MUG!
HEAD MASTER
YOU'RE JUST A DIRTY LITTLE HOOLIGAN!
IF THE NEW HEIDMASTER HADNA STOPPED US FRAE FECHTIN'—I'D PUNCH YER FACE!
YOU'RE A COWARD! YOU'RE AFRAID OF ME—THAT'S WHY!
AW! SHUT UP!
I'LL BRING MY TWO BROTHERS TO LICK YOU!
WELL, HURRY UP! I'M WANTIN' MA DENNER!
THAT'S THE LAD! HE'S NEEDIN' A BEATING UP!
THAT'S MY NEW WRESTLIN' THROW!
G-GOSH!
AN' THAT'S A BLACK EYE FOR YE!
HOWL
WE'LL TELL OUR FATHER ON YOU!
OCH! MY FAITHER'S TOUGHER THAN YOUR FAITHER!
HOWL
HO! WULLIE! I'VE FUND OOT WHA THAE THREE NEW LADS ARE! YE'LL NEVER GUESS—THEY'RE THE HEIDMASTER'S SONS!—WHIT'S WRANG WI' YE?
OH CRIVVENS! OH JINGS! I BASHED BAITH THE THREE O' THEM AT DENNER TIME!
IN SCHOOL
WILLIAM! COME HERE! I WATCHED YOU FIGHTING MY THREE SONS! AND LOOK AT THE MESS YOU'VE MADE OF THEM!
JEELY NOSE
THICK EAR
TWA BLACK EEN
JUST BECAUSE I'M YOUR FATHER YOU NEEDN'T THINK YOU CAN FIGHT AND GET AWAY WITH IT! HOLD OUT YOUR HANDS!
AS FOR YOU—I'LL DEAL WITH YOU LATER—GO TO MY PRIVATE ROOM!
BLOW
HEAD MASTER
IT'S AN AWFY FEELIN'!
YOU'RE A WEE TOPPER, WULLIE! HERE'S SIXPENCE! MY THREE LADS DESERVED ALL THEY GOT—AN' I'LL LET YOU OFF!

The Sunday Post 10th January 1943

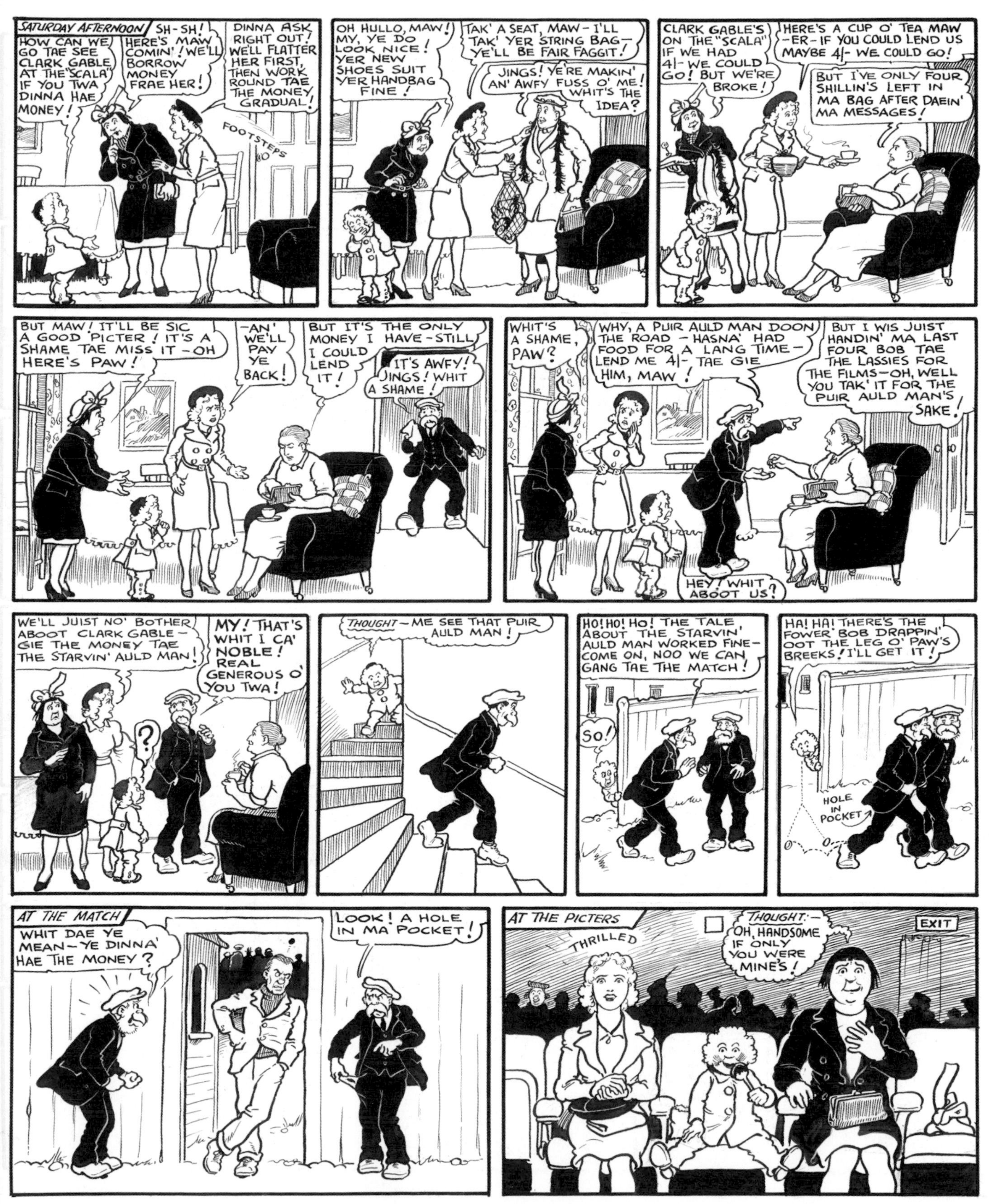

SATURDAY AFTERNOON
HOW CAN WE GO TAE SEE CLARK GABLE AT THE "SCALA" IF YOU TWA DINNA HAE MONEY!
SH-SH! HERE'S MAW COMIN'! WE'LL BORROW MONEY FRAE HER!
DINNA ASK RIGHT OUT! WE'LL FLATTER HER FIRST, THEN WORK ROUND TAE THE MONEY GRADUAL!
FOOTSTEPS
OH HULLO, MAW! MY, YE DO LOOK NICE! YER NEW SHOES SUIT YER HANDBAG FINE!
TAK' A SEAT, MAW - I'LL TAK' YER STRING BAG - YE'LL BE FAIR FAGGIT!
JINGS! YE'RE MAKIN' AN' AWFY FUSS O' ME! WHIT'S THE IDEA?
CLARK GABLE'S ON THE "SCALA" IF WE HAD 4/- WE COULD GO! BUT WE'RE BROKE!
HERE'S A CUP O' TEA MAW - ER - IF YOU COULD LEND US MAYBE 4/- WE COULD GO!
BUT I'VE ONLY FOUR SHILLIN'S LEFT IN MA BAG AFTER DAEIN' MA MESSAGES!
BUT MAW! IT'LL BE SIC A GOOD PICTER! IT'S A SHAME TAE MISS IT - OH HERE'S PAW!
-AN' WE'LL PAY YE BACK!
BUT IT'S THE ONLY MONEY I HAVE - STILL I COULD LEND IT!
IT'S AWFY! JINGS! WHIT A SHAME!
WHIT'S A SHAME, PAW?
WHY, A PUIR AULD MAN DOON THE ROAD - HASNA' HAD FOOD FOR A LANG TIME - LEND ME 4/- TAE GIE HIM, MAW!
BUT I WIS JUIST HANDIN' MA LAST FOUR BOB TAE THE LASSIES FOR THE FILMS - OH, WELL YOU TAK' IT FOR THE PUIR AULD MAN'S SAKE!
HEY! WHIT ABOOT US?
WE'LL JUIST NO' BOTHER ABOOT CLARK GABLE - GIE THE MONEY TAE THE STARVIN' AULD MAN!
MY! THAT'S WHIT I CA' NOBLE! REAL GENEROUS O' YOU TWA!
?
THOUGHT - ME SEE THAT PUIR AULD MAN!
HO! HO! HO! THE TALE ABOUT THE STARVIN' AULD MAN WORKED FINE - COME ON, NOO WE CAN GANG TAE THE MATCH!
SO!
HA! HA! THERE'S THE FOWER BOB DRAPPIN' OOT THE LEG O' PAW'S BREEKS! I'LL GET IT!
HOLE IN POCKET
AT THE MATCH
WHIT DAE YE MEAN - YE DINNA' HAE THE MONEY?
LOOK! A HOLE IN MA POCKET!
AT THE PICTERS
THRILLED
THOUGHT:- OH, HANDSOME IF ONLY YOU WERE MINE'S!
EXIT

The Sunday Post 7th March 1943

OOR WULLIE 1936-1946

AW JINGS! I'M FED UP HAEIN' TAE G'WA' TAE THE SCHOOL!
IT'S A RARE DAY. I WONDER IF I SHOULD GET SOME FRESH AIR FOR MA HEALTH THIS AFTERNOON!
AIR
I'M A GROWIN' BOY! I SHOULDNA OVER-WORK AT MA LESSONS!
CRIVVENS! I'VE WALKED INTAE THE COUNTRY! FANCY THAT NOW! I FORGOT TAE GO TAE THE SCHOOL! OH DEAR! I'LL NEED TAE PLAY TRUANT NOW!
I'LL BETTER HIDE MA SCHOOLBAG – THEN NAEBODY'LL KEN I'M PLAYIN' TRUANT!
JINGS! THAT LOOKS LIKE OOR SCHOOL ATTENDANCE OFFICER COMIN'!
TRIP
HULLO! GOT YOURSELF WET?
THOUGHT:- JINGS! I'VE HAD A RIN FOR NAETHIN HE'S NO' THE ATTENDANCE OFFICER AT A'!
10 MINUTES LATER
I'LL SOON GET DRY IN THE SUN – OH CRIVVENS! HERE COMES THE BOBBY NOW!
I CANNA GET PEACE! I'LL HIDE AHENT THIS WALL AN' PIT MA CLAES ON!
OH JINGS! LASSIES! AN' ME LIKE THIS!
HA! HA!
HO! HO!
I'LL GET IN THIS AULD BARREL, AN' GET DRESSED!
BLUSH
G-R-R RR
GROWL
NICE DOG, NICE DOG — AWA' YE GO!
STOP IT YOU! AWA' HAME! JINGS! I WISH I'D GONE TAE THE SCHOOL!
GROWL BARK
HA! HA! I'LL EASY DODGE YOU!
G-RR-RR
OH! THE GAIRDENER!
OCH! I'LL GET MA BAG AN' AWA' HAME! SCHOOL WILL BE FINISHED BY THIS TIME!
HUH! IT'S BEEN ROTTEN, PLAYIN' TRUANT! IT'S BEEN NAE FUN AT A'!
HULLO WULLIE, WHIT'S THE BIG IDEA PLAYIN' TRUANT – WE A' GOT A HOLIDAY FRAE THE SCHOOL THIS AFTERNOON!

The Sunday Post 2nd May 1943

I'M AWA' TAE SEE IF THERE'S ONY WORD ABOOT THE BOOLIN' CLUB SWEEPSTAKE! IT'S WORTH ABOOT £4!
OH GOOD! IF YE WIN IT, YE'LL HAE TAE BUY THAT BONNY STANDARD LAMP IN HENDERSON'S WINDIE! IT'S A BARGAIN AT £3-18-6!
GRAND! WE COULD DAE WI' A NICE STANDARD LAMP IN THE HOOSE!
WHIT? NO, HE'S JUST GONE OOT! WON THE SWEEPSTAKE?-OH, GOOD!! WE'LL TELL HIM!
HE'S SPEAKIN' TAE SANDY LOW!
LET'S GO AFTER HIM AN' GET HIM TAE BUY THE BONNY STANDARD LAMP AFORE SOME ITHER BODY GETS IT!
THERE HE IS- GETTIN' ON THAT TRAMCAR -EFTER HIM- QUICK!
JINGS! IT'S AWA'! COME ON, JUMP ON THIS ANE, IT'S GOIN' THE SAME WAY!
HALF AN HOUR LATER
LOOK! PAW'S TA'EN THE TRAM TAE THE TERMINUS!
JUMP OFF QUICK! AN' RIN EFTER HIM!
PAW! PAW! STOP! WAIT FOR WIS!
HEY PAW!
DADDY!
WHIT ARE YOU FOLKS YELLIN' AT!
OH CRIVVENS! IT'S NO' PAW AT A'!
I JUST FEEL DAFT!
A' THAT CHASIN' FOR NAETHIN'!
AN' I'VE GOT SAIR FEET WALKIN' BACK!
NEVER MIND, THE STANDARD LAMP IS STILL IN HENDERSON'S WINDIE! WE'LL GET IT YET, HURRY UP!
MICHTY ME! LOOK WHIT HE'S BOCHT WI' HIS SWEEPSTAKE WINNIN'S!
MAN, SANDY LOW TELT ME I WON THE SWEEPY SO I HURRIED AN' BOCHT THIS TROMBONE AFORE ONY ITHER BODY GOT IT! IT WIS A BARGAIN OOT O' HENDERSONS!

The Sunday Post 30th May 1943

PERCY PLOOK IS HAVIN' HIS BIRTHDAY PAIRTY IN HIS GAIRDEN TENT ON SATURDAY! I BET THERE'LL BE A POSH FEED!
JINGS! THAT'S GREAT! HE'LL LIKELY BE INVITIN' WIS!
WE'LL NEED TAE BUY BIRTHDAY CARDS FOR PERCY—WE CANNA' GANG TAE HIS PAIRTY WI'OUT SENDIN' HIM BIRTHDAY CARDS!
LOOK AT THE PRICE O' THEM!
THERE GOES SIX-PENCE HA'PENNY! FOWERPENCE FOR A CARD AN' TUPPENCE HA'PENNY FOR A STAMP—NOW I'LL NO BE ABLE TAE BUY ONY SWEETIES!
NEXT DAY
HULLO, PERCY! DID YE GET WIR CARDS?
YES! AND NOW I SUPPOSE I'LL HAVE TO ASK YOU TO MY PARTY! I WASN'T GOING TO AS YOU ARE SO SCRUFFY!
LATER
THAT PERCY'S A STUCK UP SNOB—BUT WE MICHT AS WEEL TAK' WIR PETS WI'S TAE DAE TRICKS AT HIS PAIRTY—THOUGH HE DISNA DESERVE IT!
JINGS! LOOK AT PERCY'S POSH GUESTS ARRIVIN'!
HULLO, PERCY! WE'VE BROCHT WIR PETS TAE DAE TRICKS!
HOWL—WOW!! THEY'VE GOT RATS AND MICE! WHAT HORRID SCRUFFY BOYS!
GET AWAY FROM US WITH THOSE FILTHY ANIMALS! YOU'RE NOT STAYING TO OUR PARTY NOW!
AW! YE STUCK UP ROTTER! EFTER US SPENDIN' A' WIR MONEY ON BIRTHDAY CARDS!
WE HOPE THAE CAKES PISENS YE!
WE'LL HAE A JOKE ON THEM—LET'S SEND WIR PETS IN AMONG THEM!
HA! HA! HA! LOOK! THEY'RE SCARED STIFF!
HOWL!
GET THOSE HORRID BEASTS OUT OF HERE—AND I'LL LET YOU COME TO MY PARTY!
NAE FEARS! YE WIDNA' KEEP YER PROMISE IF WE DID!
PLEASE GET YOUR PETS OUT—THEY'LL BE EATING ALL OUR FOOD!
MEBBE WE SHOULD GET THEM BACK! WE'LL BE LOSIN' THEM!
AYE!
JINGS! LOOK WHIT WE'VE MISSED!
AW! I'M HAEIN' A SLICE O' CAKE! TAE POT WI' PERCY!
HURRY UP AND GET THOSE VERMIN OUT OF OUR TENT!
WE'LL NO' BE LANG—WE'RE HAEIN' A JOB CATCHIN' SOAPY'S MICE!
10 MINUTES LATER
IT'S A' RICHT, PERCY! WE'VE CAPTURED THE BEASTS! AN' TAE POT WI' YER PAIRTY—YE CAN KEEP YER CAKES!
THANKS! AND I WAS ONLY KIDDING WHEN I SAID YOU COULD STAY TO MY PARTY!
WHIT DID I TELL YE?

The Sunday Post 27th June 1943

AT THE BUT AN' BEN
MY, IT'S GRAND TAE BE STAYIN' AT WIR BUT 'AN' BEN AGAIN!
AYE - BUT WHIT'S THE USE O' BEIN' OOT IN THE COUNTRY AN' SLEEPIN' INSIDE A STUFFY COTTAGE! I'D RAITHER SLEEP IN AMONG THE HEATHER! OF COURSE, YOU ANES COULDNA' DAE THAT! NANE O' YE ARE AS TOUGH AS YER AULD GRAN'FAITHER!
SEEIN' YE'RE SAE TOUGH - HERE'S SOME BLANKETS - AWA' YOU AN' SLEEP OOTSIDE THE NICHT!
HA! HA! HA! YE DIDNA' EXPECT MAW TAE TAK YE AT YER WORD!
GO ON, AWA' YE GO! LET'S SEE HOO TOUGH YE ARE!
AW - ER - WEEL, IT'S A KIND O' DULL THE NICHT - IT MICHT RAIN! OCH! BUT THAT WIDNA' BOTHER ME!
HE'LL NO' STAY OOT HAUF AN HOUR - YOU'LL SEE!
JINGS! HOO DID I HAE TAE SWANK ABOOT SLEEPIN' OOTSIDE A' NICHT! I DIDNA THINK THEY'D MAK' ME DAE IT!
AN HOUR LATER
JINGS! GRAN'PAW'S NO' BACK YET! HE'S STAYIN' OOT RICHT ENOUGH!
I HOPE HE HASNA' FALLEN DOON A HOLE!
WEEL, LET'S GET TAE BED! AN' BOLT THAT DOOR!
JINGS! IF I GANG BACK NOO, THAE ANES WILL GET AN AWFY LAUGH AT ME - BUT OH, I WID LIKE TAE BE IN MA NICE WARM BED!
SHEEP LANGUAGE -
HUH! HE THINKS HE'S A SHEEP LIKE US!
BA-AH! HE LOOKS MAIR LIKE AN' AULD GOAT TAE ME!
MY! I'VE GOT AN IDEA! I'LL AWA' BACK - SLIP INTAE BED AN' THEN SNEAK OOT IN THE MORNIN' AFORE THEY'RE UP - AN' COME BACK IN TIME FOR BREAKFAST - MY, I'LL HAE THAE ANES FAIR DIDDLED! HA! HA! HA!
THEY'VE LOCKED THE DOOR SO'S I CANNA GET BACK - BUT CAN I NO'? I'M GETTIN' IN THROUGH MA BEDROOM WINDIE!
JINGS! I CAN HARDLY SLEEP FOR LAUGHIN'! THAE DAFT IDIOTS WILL THINK I'VE SLEPT OOT A' NICHT!
EARLY NEXT MORNING
NOW I'LL PIT BACK THE BED CLAES SO THAT THEY'LL NEVER KEN THE BED'S BEEN SLEPT IN! OH, I'M FLY! BUT I'LL NEED TAE GET DRESSED QUICK OR THEY'LL CATCH ME!
I'LL AWA' AN' HIDE TILL THEY'RE UP! I'VE STRAIGHTENED MA BED AN' I'VE GOT MA BLANKETS! OCH! THEY'LL NEVER KEN I'VE SLEPT IN THE HOOSE!
BREAKFAST TIME
HI! YOU YINS! YE DINNA KEN WHIT YE'VE MISSED! IT WIS RARE SLEEPIN' OOT A' NICHT!
OH YEAH? WE KEN FINE YE WISNA' OOT A' NICHT - COME INTAE YER BEDROOM -
- THOUGH YE MADE YER BED FINE WHEN YE WENT OOT THIS MORNIN', YE MADE WAN MISTAKE - YE FORGOT TAE PIT ON YER AULD COMBINATIONS WHEN YE GOT UP!
AN' THEY NEED WASHIN' TAE!

The Sunday Post 27th June 1943

HULLO, WULLIE! DAE YE KEN WE'RE GETTIN' MARRIED ON TUESDAY?
WE WOULD HAVE ASKED YOU TO COME IF WE'D REMEMBERED!
JINGS! THAT'S GREAT!
OCH! I'LL GANG TAE THEIR MARRIAGE AS A SURPRISE! THAY WAD LIKE ME TAE COME! THEY JUIST FORGOT TAE ASK ME!
I'M GAUN TAE A WEDDIN' ON TUESDAY! I WISNA ASKED RICHT, THEY SAID THEY FORGOT A' ABOOT ME!
OH WEEL, YE'LL NEED TAE WEAR A TAILIE COAT AN' A TILE HAT TAE A WEDDIN'!
NOW, WHAUR COULD I GET A TAILIE COAT AN' A TILE HAT MY SIZE?
OCH! I KEN! — TAMMY DODD'S FAITHER'S A WEE MAN. I'LL GET HIS!
HERE, TAMMY, I'LL GIE YE THIS PEERIE AN' FOWER BOOLS AN' A KNIFE AN' MA CATTY IF YOU GET ME A LEN O' YER FAITHER'S TILE HAT AN' TAILIE COAT FOR TUESDAY!
O.K. WULLIE!
TUESDAY
HERE'S THE CLAES, WULLIE!
THANKS, TAMMY!
2 p.m
JINGS! I'M GAUN TAE LOOK A REAL TOFF!
HEY YOU! IT'S NO' GUISERS NICHT YET!
POSH
-BUT YE CANNA COME IN HERE - YE DINNA HAE A PROPER INVITATION CAIRD!
ASSEMBLY HALLS DANCES, RECEPTIONS WEDDINGS, LECTURES
AW— JINGS!
HUH! TAE POT WI' HIM— I'LL CLIMB IN THIS WINDIE!
HERE I AM! I CAM' AS A SURPRISE TAE YE!
THE BRIDE MUST CUT THE CAKE!
JINGS! THE WRANG MARRIAGE!!
!
THERE'S ANITHER MARRIAGE IN THE EAST HALL ALANG THERE, BUT IT STARTED AN HOUR AGO!
BLUSH
IS THIS ALLY BUCHAN AN' MAG WILSON'S MARRIAGE IN HERE?
AYE, AN' IT'S GEY DULL— THERE'S AN AULD FOGEY RECITIN' AN'SHE WINNA STOP! NAE FUN AT A'!
YAP-YAP
CONGRATULATIONS! I JUIST CAM TAE GIE YE A SURPRISE!
WHY! IT'S THAT CHEERY LAD-OOR WULLIE!
GET HIM TAE SING AN' CHEER UP THE GUESTS!
I CANNA SING GOOD, BUT I'LL GIE YE A TUNE ON MA MOUTHIE AN' A WEE BIT DANCE!
HA! HA!
TAP DANCE
THAT WIS FINE, WULLIE. YE'VE SET THE BALL ROLLIN'. EVERYBODY'S DANCIN' SO TUCK IN TAE WHIT'S LEFT O' THE WEDDIN' FEAST! WE'VE HAD OURS!
OH, BOY! THANKS ALLY AN' MAG!
JINGS! MARRIAGES ARE A' RICHT! I'LL NEED TAE LOOK OOT FOR A DAME!

The Sunday Post 3rd October 1943

JINGS! WHIT A POOR FIRE!
AN' IN THIS CAULD WEATHER!
WE'LL NEED TAE GET SOME LOGS TAE HELP OOT THE COAL—IF YOU ANES GET THE CHANCE, BRING IT HAME OR ORDER IT!
I'LL GET YE SOME!
NO HEAT
EVEN THE KETTLE'S SHIVERIN'!
NEXT DAY
OH—ER—GOOD MORNING—WE NEED SOME FIRE-WOOD AT HOME! COULD YOU LET ME HAVE SOME!
OH YES, MISS, WE'RE SHORT OF FIREWOOD BUT I CAN TALK THE BOSS ROUND INTO LETTING YOU HAVE ANY AMOUNT! I'LL BRING IT UP MYSELF!
BLUSH
SHOWING OFF
HULLO! IT'S BIG WULL SMITH SELLIN' FIREWID! HERE, I'LL BUY THE LOT AFF YE WULL—TAK' IT UP TAE OOR HOOSE NOW!
O.K., DAPHNE!
THOUGHT:— MAW'LL BE GLAD TAE GET THIS LOAD!
WHO'S THAT DIRTY LOOKING OLD MAN, IS HE A BEGGAR?
NO, BUT ISN'T HE ORRA?—HE'S THAT MR BROON'S AULD FAITHER! HE'S A DISGRACE TO THE FAMILY!
KIRKGATE
RATTLE
I'M GOIN' OUT, SO IF ONY MESSAGES COME, PIT THEM ON THE TABLE!—AN' DINNA FORGET TAE KEEP A DECENT FIRE!
O.K., MAW!
LATER
HULLO, WULL! YOU BRINGIN' WOOD TAE THE BROONS TAE?
MAN, AYE, I'VE A BARRY LOAD DOON THERE FOR THEM!
IS MISS MAGGIE BROON IN? I'VE BROCHT SOME LOGS FOR HER!—THERE'S MAIR DOON THE STAIR!
OH, THANKS, BRING IT IN!
HORACE BROON LOVES JESSIE GORDON
CRIVVENS! WHIT'S A' THIS! LOGS! MICHTY ME!!
AYE, THERE WIS THAT MONY WE COULDNA GET THEM A' ON THE TABLE, MAW!
AN' WE'VE KEPT A GUID FIRE LIKE YE SAID!
HEAT
JINGS! HOW ARE YE NO' SITTIN' OWER THE FIRE? LAST TIME I WIS IN, YE WIS COMPLAININ' ABOOT THE CAULD! I'VE BROCHT YE SOME FIREWID!
HEAT
MICHTY ME! DINNA MENTION FIREWID!
ME SWEATIN'!

The Sunday Post 19th December 1943

HULLO, WULLIE, WILL YE HAUD MA PIG UNTIL I GET SOME BACCY?—I'M JUIST AWA' TAE MARKET TAE SELL IT, I'LL LIKELY GET £10 FOR IT!
TOBACCONIST
O.K. MR WALLACE!
LOOK! I'LL GIE YE A SHOT AT PULLIN' ME IN MA BARROW, PIGGIE!
JINGS! THIS IS GREAT!
HEY! WAIT A MEENIT! YE CANNA GO INTAE A SHOP!
DEPARTMENT STORES
CLOTHING
GROCERY
RESTAURANT
BOOTS AND SHOES
STOP! STOP! YE WEE PIG. YE!
BOOTS AND SHOES
COME BACK- YE'VE NAE RICHT IN HERE!
HATS CAPS GLOVES TIES ETC.
HATS
YOU'VE MADE A GOOD JOB OF PILING UP THOSE TINS, JOSEPH!
THANK YOU, SIR!
GROCERY DEPT →
HOI!
HI!
GROCERY DEPT →
BLOGG'S TEA
SWOOSH
BANG!
GROCERY DEPT
TO RESTAURANT
RESTAURANT GROUND FLOOR
MILLINERY FIRST FLOOR
HARDWARE
JINGS! YE GAE ME A ROUGH PASSAGE BUT IT WIS GOOD FUN!
MAN! THAT'S A FINE PIG! I'LL BUY IT AFF YE AN' GIE YE THE TOP MARKET PRICE!
RIGHT! IT'S A DEAL!
LATER
WHAUR'VE YE BEEN? AN' WHAUR'S MA PIG? I'VE BEEN LOOKIN' FOR YE FOR TWA HOURS!
IT'S A' RICHT! I'VE SELL'T IT!
WALLACE
SELL'T IT! YE MUST HAE BEEN SWINDLED—AN' I COULD HAE GOT £10 FOR'T
LOOK! £12-10- AN' NAE BOTHER!!
THAT'S RICHT, MAW! GIE WULLIE FOWER BILED EGGS FOR HIS TEA!

The Sunday Post 14th November 1943

THE MORN AN' WE'LL GO FOR A HIKE!
TIME!
O.K!
DAY
BUT I'M GOIN' HIKIN' JUST THE SAME! I'LL PIT ON MA WEE CYCLIN' CAPE!
READY FOR THE ROAD?
GOIN' A HIKE THIS RAIN!
WULLIE

1944

THE WEE SPITFIRE

WHILE Oor Wullie was doing his bit for the war effort by keeping the country laughing, the legendary Spitfire aircraft was fighting the war in the air. But it's not so well known that Wullie and the Spitfire are exactly the same age. The Spitfire had its first test flight the same week as the first Oor Wullie strip appeared in the Sunday Post and, like Wullie, the Spitfire is still going strong. At the time of writing in Spring 2006 there are more Spitfires flying now than at any time since the Second World War.

OOR WULLIE 1936-1946

MA! CAN I SIT UP AN' SEE THE NEW YEAR IN, AN' WISH A' WIR VISITORS A-HAPPY NEW YEAR AN' A BOTTLE O' BEER AN' A SKELP IN THE EAR FOR NEXT NEW YEAR?
NO! YE'RE FAR TOO WEE! BED FOR YOU AT TEN PAST TWEL'!
HOGMANAY
JINGS! I'M WEARY FOR THE NEW YEAR! WILL IT BE LANG?
TWA HOURS WULLIE!
11.30 P.M.
FAST ASLEEP
WAKE UP, WULLIE! IT'S STRIKIN' TWEL' — IT'S THE NEW YEAR!
EH? - YAWN — HAPPY NEW YEAR, MA—!
12-15 AM. 1st JAN. 1944
JINGS! I'M TIRED — I'M AWA' TAE MA BED!
THERE'S OOR FIRST FEET ACH I'LL WISH A'BODY A HAPPY NEW YEAR THE MORN!
HAPPY NEW YEAR
COME IN COME IN
9. A.M. 1st JAN. 1944
JINGS! NAEBODY UP YET!
HAPPY NEW YEAR
I'M TOO TIRED TAE RISE! MAK' YER AIN BREAKFAST WULLIE!
MICHTY ME!
JINGS! IT'S CAULD WI' NAE FIRE ON - I'VE BURNT THE BACON AN' THE TEA'S OWER STRONG!
CAULD
I'LL AWA AN' WISH MA CHUMS A HAPPY NEW YEAR!
TIRED
CHIPS
HAPPY NEW YEAR BOB!
IT'S OWER EARLY - HOO CAN YE NO' LET ME SLEEP! I WIS UP TILL FOWER!
HUH! TAE POT WI' BOB I'LL AWA AN' SEE SOAPY SOUTAR!
HAPPY NEW YEAR, SOAPY!
YE'VE GOT A CHEEK WAKENIN' ME AS EARLY AS THIS!
JINGS! WHA'S THAT KNOCKIN' AT THE DOOR AT THIS EARLY HOUR! OH, IT'S YOU WULLIE - HAPPY NEW YEAR -
HAPPY NEW YEAR, UNCLE TAM!
GOOD MORNIN' MR HEID MESTER! HAPPY NEW YEAR!
DON'T BOTHER ME NOW — I HAD THE TEACHERS HERE TILL 3-30 A.M.!
JINGS! WHIT A LOT O' FROSTS A' BODY IS THIS MORNIN' — I'LL JUIST TRY P.C. MURDOCH AN' IF HE'S GIRNY TAE — I'LL AWA BACK TAE BED AS WELL!
HAPPY NEW YEAR MESTER MURDOCH!
GLAD TAE SEE YE, WULLIE! HAPPY NEW YEAR!
WHIT BRINGS YOU OOT SAE EARLY IN THE MORNIN'!
I WIS ON THE LATE SHIFT LAST NICHT AN' I SLEPT IN TILL 9 O'CLOCK AN' MISSED THE NEW YEAR COMIN' IN - SO I'M AWA TAE FIRST FOOT A'BODY NOW!
WEEL YE NEEDNA BOTHER - I'VE BEEN ROUND THEM A' AN' THEY'RE JUIST A LOT O' GREETIN' FACED GIRNIN' GROUSERS - THIS MORNIN' - A' EXCEPT YOU!
AH! WEEL! TAE POT WI' THEM WULLIE! YOU AN' ME'LL HAE OOR NEW YEAR THEGITHER - DRINK UP - YOU CAN HAE A' THE GINGER WINE AN' CORDIAL - I'LL HAE THE ITHER STUFF -!
HERE'S TAE US! WHA'S LIKE US!
JINGS! WHIT A GREAT NEW YEAR I'VE HAD!

The Sunday Post 2nd January 1944

AT THE BUT AN' BEN
WE'VE JUIST ENOUGH WI' THIS BIT O' HAM TAE DAE US FOR A' OOR FOOD THE DAY!
WE'LL GO FOR A WALK THIS FORENOON AN' COME BACK AN' FINISH THE HAM!
I HOPE GRAN' PAW DOESNA COME HERE — HE'S AYE HUNGRY!
HURRY UP!
AN HOUR LATER
ONYBODY IN? I'M FAIR STARVIN'! I WIS UP EARLY AN' WALKED A' THE ROAD ---- WHIT? NAE ANSWER? .... HUH! THEY'RE A' OOT!
OCH! BUT I CAN HELP MASEL'! IT'S LUCKY THEY'VE LEFT THIS HAM ON THE TABLE — MAYBE THEY EXPECTED ME!
½ AN HOUR LATER
MY! THAT WIS A GRAND SNACK. I'LL MAK' SOME SAN'WICHES WI' THE HAM, THEN GO FOR A WALK, TAE GET AN APPETITE FOR MA TEA!
WEEL, THAT'S MA HAM SAN'WICHES PACKED — I'LL LEAVE A NOTE ON THE TABLE!
LOOK! GRAN' PAW'S BEEN HERE AN LEFT A NOTE. HE SAYS "I'VE TOOK SOME O' YER HAM BUT I'LL BE BACK FOR MA TEA, SO SEE AN' HAE A BIG FEED READY." WHIT A CHEEK!
HE'S NEARLY FINISHED THE HAM!
JINGS! THIS RAIN'S SOAKIN' ME! I THINK I'M TAKIN' THE CAULD — I'LL BE GLAD TAE GET BACK TAE THE BUT AN' BEN!
OH DEAR! I'M SOAKED AN' IT'S GIVEN ME A DOSE O' THE CAULD!
HUH! IT SERVES YE RICHT FOR TAKIN' A' THE HAM! AN' NOW WI' YER CAULD, YE'LL NO' FEEL LIKE EATIN'!
WILL I NO'? YE KEN THE AULD SAYIN' — "STUFF A CAULD, STARVE A FEVER" — OH! I'M GOIN' TAE SNEEZE — A-A-A-A —
-A-A-A-TISHOO-OO!!!
GERMS
CRASH
HA! HA! HA! HE'S SNEEZED OOT HIS FALSE TEETH — NOW HE CANNA EAT!
WEEL, YE CAN STUFF YERSEL' WI' GRUEL! IT'S WHIT YE NEED WI' A CAULD — AN' YE CANNA EAT ONYTHING SOLID SINCE YE'VE BROKEN YER FALSE TEETH! WE'LL EAT THE REST O' THE HAM!
MISERY

The Sunday Post 5th March 1944

RIGHT! I'LL MEET YE HERE THE MORN AN' WE'LL GO FOR A HIKE!
BE ON TIME!
O.K.!
NEXT DAY
JINGS! IT'S RAININ' BUT I'M GOIN' HIKIN' JUST THE SAME! I'LL PIT ON MA WEE CYCLIN' CAPE!
WEEL, ARE YE READY FOR THE ROAD?
WHIT! YE'RE SURELY NO' GOIN' A HIKE IN A' THIS RAIN!
SURE! I'M NO' A SISSY LIKE YOU TWA! I'LL GO MASEL! I'LL SHOW YE!
I BET YE SNEAK BACK HAME AS SOON AS YE'RE OOT O' SICHT!
HUH! TAE PROVE TAE YE I'VE BEEN OOT, I'LL TELL YE WHIT I'VE SEEN WHEN I GET BACK!
CLANK
JINGS! IT'S AWFY HEAVY RAIN. OCH! I'LL AWA' BACK, BUT I'LL NO' GO NEAR FAT BOB AN' THEM — I'LL GO TAE THE CINEMA AN' EAT MA PIECE IN THERE!
BALCONY
ONE FOURPENNY, PLEASE!
GOODY! A TRAVEL PICTER! LOOK AT THE EPHELUNTS!
OOOH!! RHINOCOSSEROSSES OR HOPPOPITAMUSES! NO, THEY'RE GIRAFFUSES!
BOY! A MAN SHOOTIN' A TIGER CHASIN' A COO!
AW! THIS IS ANE O' THAE CAKEY LOVE PICTERS! I'LL EAT MA PIECE NOW!
LATER
I HOPE FAT BOB AN' SOAPY SOUTAR ARE NO' HANGIN' ABOUT TAE SEE ME COMIN' OOT!
2 HOURS LATER
WEEL, HOO DID YE ENJOY YER HIKE OOT IN THE RAIN? YE DINNA LOOK VERY WEET! I BET YER PIECE WIS A' SOAKIN'!
OH-ER-I- IT WISNA RAININ' WHAUR I WIS — I GOT A RARE DRY PLACE TAE EAT MA PIECE!
YE SAID YE'D TELL US WHIT YE SAW WHEN YE GOT BACK!
EH? OH JINGS - SO I DID - OH MY!
THOUGHT:- WHIT'LL I TELL THEM?
WEEL, FIRST I SAW A HERD O' WILD ELEPHANTS, THEN A LOT O' GIRAFFES RINNIN' LIKE MAD — OOH — AN' THEN A TIGER CHASIN' A KIND O' A STAG AN' A MAN SHOT THE TIGER JUST IN TIME! MAN! IT WIS A GREAT SICHT - YOU LADS MISSED YERSEL'S!
YE SAW THAT ON THE FILMS — AN' WE DIDNA MISS WIRSELS NEITHER - FOR WE SAW THAT PICTER JUST EFTER YOU!
WH- WHIT! EH? JINGS!
FORBYE, YE DINNA SEE ELEPHANTS, GIRAFFES AN' TIGERS RINNIN' ABOOT WILD IN SCOTLAND - AN' WHIT'S MAIR YE LEFT YER CAPE WI' YER NAME ON IT UNDER THE FRONT ROW O' THE FOWERPENNIES!
WULLIE
SHAME
HA! HA! HA!!

The Sunday Post 19th March 1944

JINGS! WHIT A MEASLEY TEA TAE GIE ME WHEN I COME TAE SEE YE! WAN SARDINE ON A SLICE O' TOAST!
WEEL, HOO DID YE NO' LET ME KEN YE WIS COMIN? BESIDES I'M IN A HURRY TAE GET DOON THE ROAD!
I'M MAD AT MAW! WHIT A WELCOME! WHIT A TEA!
I'VE GOT AN IDEA! I'LL PLAY A JOKE ON MAW— AN' GET A GOOD TEA INTAE THE BARGAIN!
NEXT MORNING
LOOK! I'VE GOT SIX LETTERS THE DAY! ANE FRAE GRAN' PAW, AN' THE ITHERS FRAE AUNT LIZZIE, AUNT JESSIE, MRS LOW, COUSIN JEANNIE IN AUCHENTOGLE, AND MRS GRAY! - AN' THEY A' SAY THEY'RE COMIN' FOR THEIR TEA THE DAY!
WHIT A CROWD! FANCY THEM A' PICKIN' THE SAME DAY! WE'LL NEED TAE GET A LOT O' FOOD IN FOR THEM!
THAT AFTERNOON
AHA! I SEE YE GOT MA LETTER! AN' I SEE YE'VE GOT A GUID TEA SET, READY FOR ME THIS TIME! MY! A HALE TIN O' SARDINES OOT, A TIN O' SALMON — CAKES, SCONES — AN' I CAN SMELL KIPPERS COOKIN'!
KIPPERS
SIZZLE
HUH! YE NEEDNA THINK YOU'RE GETTIN' A' THAT! THERE'S FIVE OTHER FOLKS COMIN' TAE!
HA! HA! HA! THAT'S WHIT YOU THINK! THERE'S NAEBODY TAE COME BUT ME! I SENT YE THAE LETTERS — FRAE AUNT LIZZIE, AUNT JESSIE MRS LOW, COUSIN JEANNIE AN' MRS GRAY! — SO'S YE'D BE SURE TAE GET PLENTY O' THINGS IN! HA! HA! HA!
WHIT! OH - YE FLY AULD FIFER! YE WEE TATTIE-BOGLE-YE TWISTER YE!!!
OH MAW! I'VE BROCHT MA FIVE CHUMS IN FOR WIR TEA! WE'VE CYCLED 40 MILES AN' WE'VE A' GOT THE KNOCK' — WE'RE STARVIN'!
YE SEE! GUESTS EFTER A'! AN' HUNGRY CYCLISTS AT THAT!
GOOD FOR YOU, MAW! YE'VE GOT THE TABLE SET JUIST AS IF YE WIS EXPECTIN' US!
I'M FAIR FAMISHED!
HEY! LEAVE SOME O' THAE SARDINES TAE ME!
THAT'S YER FIFTH SCONE, JOCK! CA CANNY!
YER FLYNESS HASNA' DONE YE ONY GOOD! - YE'VE JUIST GOT WHIT YE HAD LAST TIME — IT'S A' THERE IS LEFT — A SARDINE ON TOAST!
!
GRAN'PAW'S SARDINE EATEN—
OCH! I'LL NO' BE OWER HARD ON YE! HERE'S A COUPLE O' KIPPERS! I'M THAT RELIEVED THAT AUNT JESSIE AN' AUNT LIZZIE AN' THEM ARE NO' REALLY COMIN' — FOR THEY AYE FECHT WHEN THEY GET THEGITHER!

The Sunday Post 9th April 1944

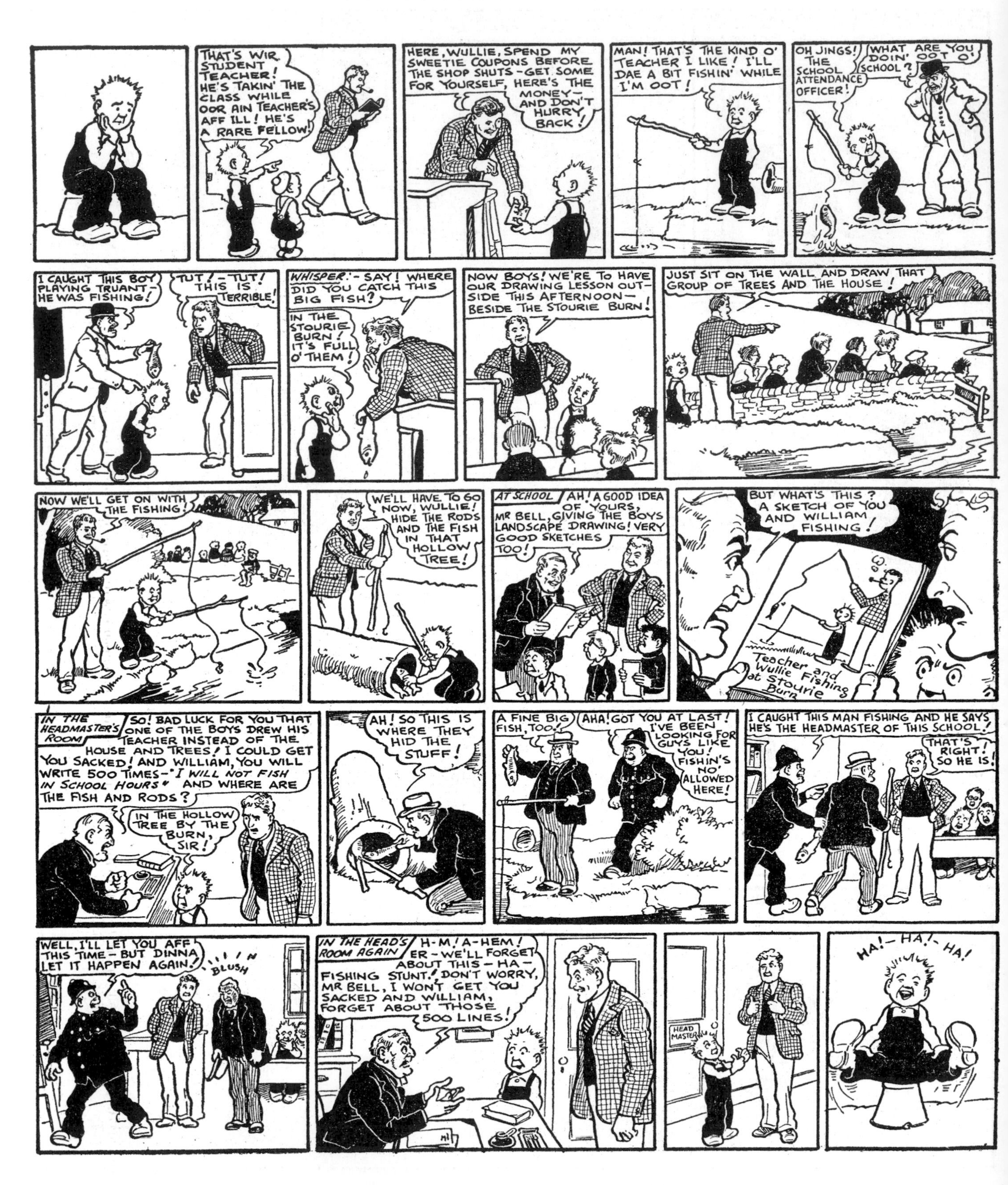
THAT'S WIR STUDENT TEACHER! HE'S TAKIN' THE CLASS WHILE OOR AIN TEACHER'S AFF ILL! HE'S A RARE FELLOW!
HERE, WULLIE, SPEND MY SWEETIE COUPONS BEFORE THE SHOP SHUTS - GET SOME FOR YOURSELF, HERE'S THE MONEY - AND DON'T HURRY BACK!
MAN! THAT'S THE KIND O' TEACHER I LIKE! I'LL DAE A BIT FISHIN' WHILE I'M OOT!
OH JINGS! THE SCHOOL ATTENDANCE OFFICER!
WHAT ARE YOU DOIN' OOT O' SCHOOL?
I CAUGHT THIS BOY PLAYING TRUANT - HE WAS FISHING!
TUT! - TUT! THIS IS TERRIBLE!
WHISPER: - SAY! WHERE DID YOU CATCH THIS BIG FISH?
IN THE STOURIE BURN! IT'S FULL O' THEM!
NOW BOYS! WE'RE TO HAVE OUR DRAWING LESSON OUTSIDE THIS AFTERNOON - BESIDE THE STOURIE BURN!
JUST SIT ON THE WALL AND DRAW THAT GROUP OF TREES AND THE HOUSE!
NOW WE'LL GET ON WITH THE FISHING!
WE'LL HAVE TO GO NOW, WULLIE! HIDE THE RODS AND THE FISH IN THAT HOLLOW TREE!
AT SCHOOL
AH! A GOOD IDEA OF YOURS, MR BELL, GIVING THE BOYS LANDSCAPE DRAWING! VERY GOOD SKETCHES TOO!
BUT WHAT'S THIS? A SKETCH OF YOU AND WILLIAM FISHING!
Teacher and Wullie Fishing at Stourie Burn
IN THE HEADMASTER'S ROOM
SO! BAD LUCK FOR YOU THAT ONE OF THE BOYS DREW HIS TEACHER INSTEAD OF THE HOUSE AND TREES! I COULD GET YOU SACKED! AND WILLIAM, YOU WILL WRITE 500 TIMES - "I WILL NOT FISH IN SCHOOL HOURS" AND WHERE ARE THE FISH AND RODS?
IN THE HOLLOW TREE BY THE BURN, SIR!
AH! SO THIS IS WHERE THEY HID THE STUFF!
A FINE BIG FISH, TOO!
AHA! GOT YOU AT LAST! I'VE BEEN LOOKING FOR GUYS LIKE YOU! FISHIN'S NO' ALLOWED HERE!
I CAUGHT THIS MAN FISHING AND HE SAYS HE'S THE HEADMASTER OF THIS SCHOOL!
THAT'S RIGHT! SO HE IS!
WELL, I'LL LET YOU AFF THIS TIME - BUT DINNA LET IT HAPPEN AGAIN!
BLUSH
IN THE HEAD'S ROOM AGAIN
H-M! A-HEM! ER - WE'LL FORGET ABOUT THIS - HA - FISHING STUNT! DON'T WORRY, MR BELL, I WON'T GET YOU SACKED AND WILLIAM, FORGET ABOUT THOSE 500 LINES!
HEAD MASTER
HA! - HA! - HA!

The Sunday Post 17th September 1944

WE'VE LEFT THE AULD EASY CHAIR, THE FENDER, AN' A' THING THAT YE'RE BUYIN' AFF US, ON THE BACK GREEN. WE'RE AWA' TAE THE PICTERS!
O.K.! I'LL SEND THE LAD ROOND FOR THEM WI' THE BARROW!
Second Hand Furniture Bought & Sold
TAK' THE BARROW AN' COLLECT A' THE STUFF ON THE BACK GREEN AT 10 GLEBE STREET!
ANTIQUES
O.K.
CINEMA
AHA! ME PLAY HOOSES WI' THAE!
NOW YOU DOLLIES SIT THERE TILL ME GET A BASIN TAE BATH YE IN!
HERE, LET'S GET SOME MAIR CHAIRS AN' THINGS OOT O' THE HOOSE, AN' MAK' A TRAMCAR!
AYE - AN' WE'LL GET A' WIR PALS TAE PLAY!
FARES PLEASE!
HOO CAN YE NO COME FOR IT UP THE STAIRS!
DING DING!
HEY, YOU! ME WANT TAE PLAY HOOSES!
HEY! YOU KIDS! GET AFF O' THAT! I'VE TAE TAK' A' THING TAE THE SHOP, YER MAW SAYS SO!
I GET AFF AT THE NEXT STOP!
LATER
JINGS! THE KITCHEN'S AWFY BARE - WHAUR'S A' WIR STUFF GONE?
WE WIS PLAYIN' TRAMCARS AN' HOOSES ON THE BACK GREEN AN' THE FURNITURE LAD TOOK A' THE STUFF AWA' ON HIS BARROW!
MICHTY! HE WIS TELT TAE TAK' A' THING - AN' HE DID! WE'LL NEED TAE GET IT BACK!
LOOK! A MOONLICHT FLITTIN'!
GLEBE STREET
GLARE
WHIT HAE YOU GOT TAE LAUGH AT?

The Sunday Post 12th November 1944

THEY'RE VISITORS FRAE LONDON! THE LADDIE'S AWFIE WEEL SPOKEN AN' NICE MANNERED - NO' A WEE SCRUFF LIKE YOU WULLIE, SPEAKIN' ORRA AN' PLAYIN' WI' ROUGH LADDIES!
I'LL ASK HIM AN' HIS MA TAE THEIR TEA! THEN YE'LL MAYBE LEARN TAE SPEAK BETTER AN' BE MAIR POLITE!
NEXT DAY
HOW DO YOU DO!
HI-YA PAL!
RAISE
WIPE
I'M VERY PLEASED TO MEET YOU!
AW! THAT'S A'RICHT! NAE BOTHER AT A'!
IT'LL BE AN AWFY POSH SCHOOL YOU'LL BE AT? I JUST GANG TAE THE RAGGED SCHOOL!
OH YES, WE HAVE A JOLLY GOOD SET OF FELLOWS, RUGGER AND ALL THAT!
COME ON, CLARENCE, SIT YE DOON, TEA'S READY - GET MUCKED IN!
OH-ER-IT'S NOT POLITE TO SIT AT THE TABLE BEFORE THE LADIES ARE SEATED!
RED FACE
THOUGHT:- JINGS! IT WID TAK' AN AWFY LOT O' DAEIN' TAE BE POSH LIKE CLARENCE BUT I'LL TRY, JUST TAE PLEASE MA!
DAINTY
NOW GO OUT AND PLAY WITH WILLIAM, HE'LL SHOW YOU ROUND!
WHISPER:- WHILE YE'RE OOT-WATCH HOW HE SPEAKS AN' DOES THINGS! AN' TRY AN' BE POSH LIKE HIM!
YES, MOTHER!
O.K. MA!
MY MA SAYS I'VE GOT TAE LEARN TAE BE WEEL MANNERED AN' WEEL SPOKEN LIKE YOUS!
OH! THAT'S EASY! I WISH I COULD SPEAK LIKE YOU AN' I WISH I HAD DUNGAREES LIKE YOU!
I'LL FIX YE UP WI' AN AULD PAIR O' DUNGAREES, THEN WE'LL PLAY WI' FAT BOB AN' SOAPY SOUTAR AN' YE'LL HEAR THE REAL BROAD SCOTCH!
WULLIE'S Shed
-AN' I'LL PIT ON YER CAP AN' YER BLAZER!
I'LL PRACTISE SPEAKIN' POSH! PLEASTERMEETCHA! HOO'S YER AULD MAN - I MEAN - YER FAITHER? PARDON ME, I TROD ON YER FUT! NA! NA! THAT'S AWFY!
SHAKE
JINGS! CRIVVENS! HA! HA! I'LL LEARN YOUR WAY O' SPEAKIN' YET!
GOOD EFTERNUNE MISTRESS FAIRWEATHER! HOW'S YER SAIR-SORE-FEET?
OH! HULLO, ALEXANDER! REALLY, OLD BOY! CHARMED TO SEE YOU, OLD MAN!
WEE ECK
ECK DOESN'T UNDERSTAND US POSH FELLOWS!
RASP
I'M GLAD WULLIE AN' CLARENCE ARE PLAYING TOGETHER! CLARENCE WILL SET WULLIE SUCH A GOOD EXAMPLE - WULLIE IS SO ROUGH!
HELLO, MATER, BAI GOSH! REALLY! CLARENCE AND I HAVE HAD A TOPPING TIME! JOLLY GOOD SPORT, CLARENCE! HE'S TALKING TO FAT BOB AND SOAPY SOUTAR! HE'LL BE HERE ANON!
HEY! YOU YINS! JINGS, WE'VE HAD A RARE TIME! CRIVVENS! I WIS PLAYIN' BOOLS WI' FAT BOB AN' SOAPY SOUTAR! THEN WE HAD A DANDY GAME O' TIG IN THE MIDDEN!
SWANKY

The Sunday Post 22nd October 1944

JINGS! THERE'S NAE PLEASIN' SOME FOWK!

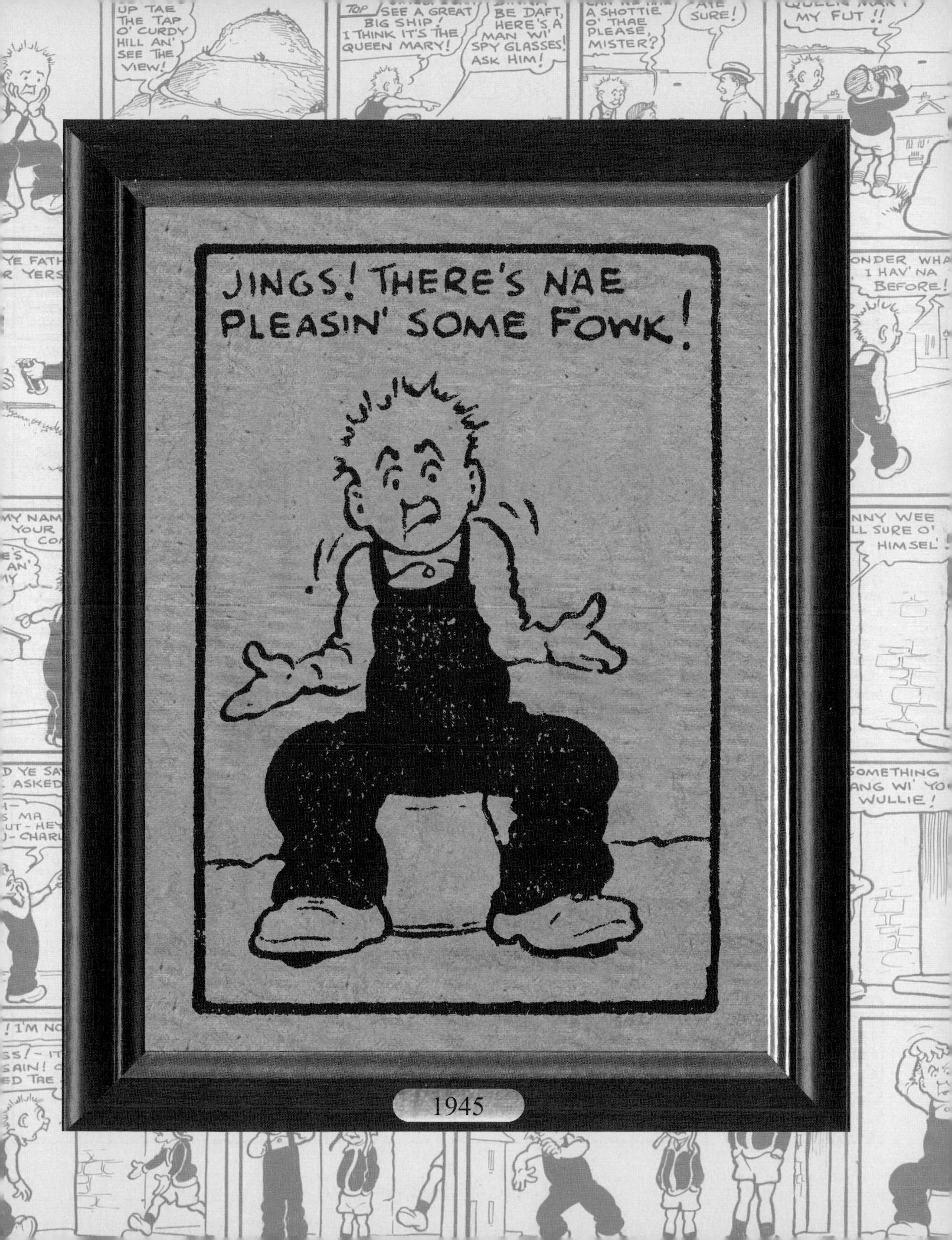

1945

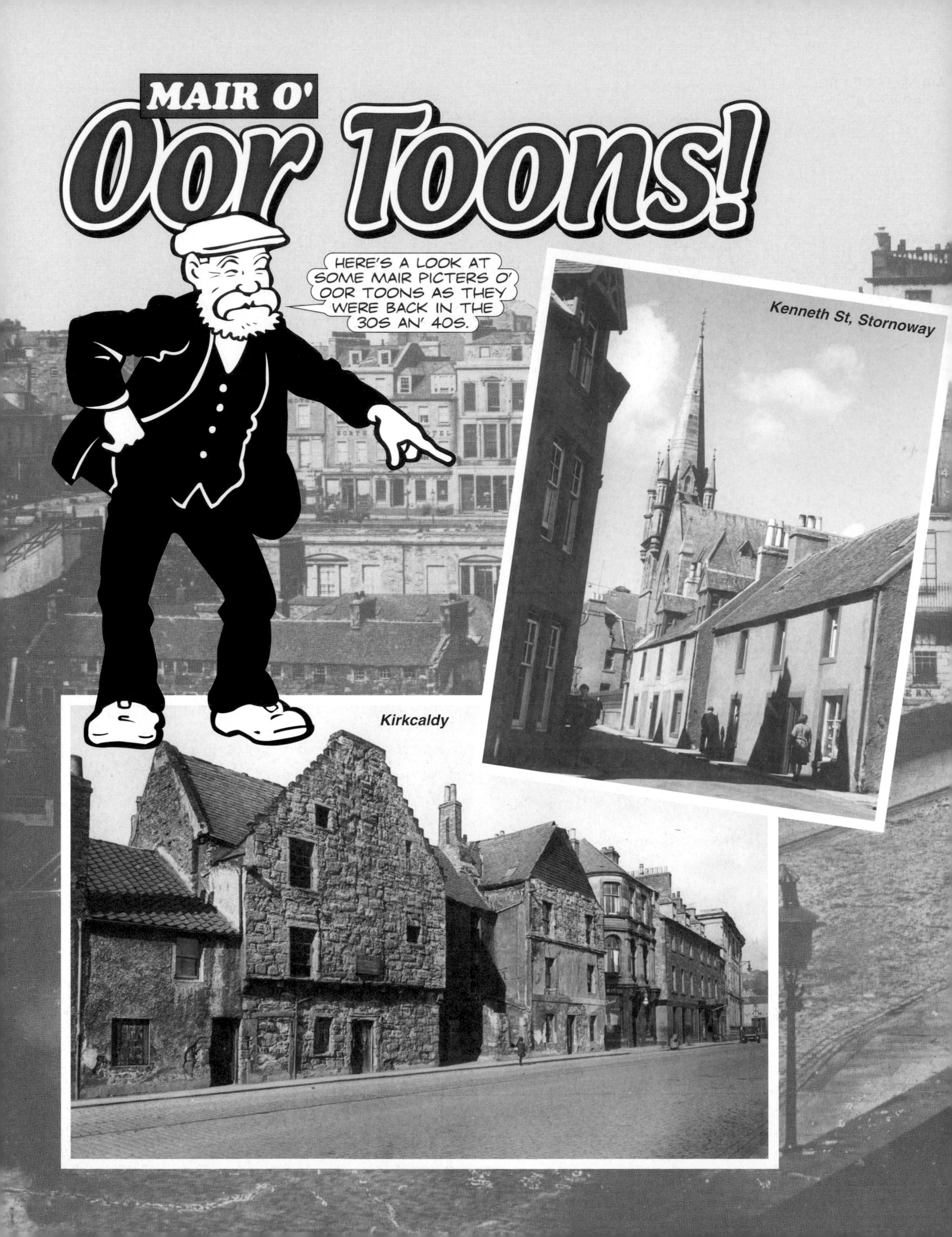
MAIR O'
Oor Toons!
HERE'S A LOOK AT SOME MAIR PICTERS O' OOR TOONS AS THEY WERE BACK IN THE 30S AN' 40S.
Kenneth St, Stornoway
Kirkcaldy

Looking into Old Edinburgh

Kintillo, which was Scotland's auldest village

The Last Wall and Tower at the Old Fort, Ayr

The Old Bridge, Stirling

JINGS! DEEP SNAW! THIS IS GREAT! I'LL AWA' AN' GET FAT BOB AN' SOAPY AN' WE'LL HAE GREAT FUN!
AT BOB'S
NA, WULLIE, MA'LL NO' LET ME OOT, SHE'S FEARED I GET THE CAULD!
HUH!
BOB'S A SISSY! I'LL AWA' ROOND AN' GET SOAPY SOUTAR!
NO' ME, WULLIE - I'M NO' COMIN' OOT TAE PLAY THE DAY, IT'S OWER CAULD!
JINGS! YOU'RE A PANSY TAE! YE SHOULD BE TOUGH LIKE ME!
HUH! FAT BOB AN' SOAPY CANNA STAND THE CAULD LIKE ME! I'LL TRY A BIT SKATIN'!
I'LL NEED TAE GO ON HANDS AND KNEES TILL I MIND HOO TAE SKATE AGAIN! I'M GLAD BOB AN' SOAPY ARE NO' HERE TAE SEE ME!
JINGS! SHE'S GOOD! HUH! IF A WEE LASSIE CAN DAE THAT - SURELY I CAN!
OCH AYE - IT'S EASY -
GOSH! IT'S NO' SAE EASY!
CRASH
10 MINUTES LATER
NOW IF I FA' DOON AGAIN I'LL NO' HURT MASEL'!
JINGS! I FELL THE WRANG WAY! - OCH! TAE POT WI' SKATES, I'LL AWA' AN' GET A SLEDGE!
SLEDGIN'S MAIR IN MY LINE! SKATIN'S SISSY!
WO-OO-OW!
AW- SORRY!
SORRY, ARE YE? I'LL MAK' YE MAIR SORRY!
CRASH
CRACK
SPLASH
MAD
MA! OPEN THE DOOR! LET'S IN! YER PUIR WULLIE'S TURNIN' INTAE AN ICICLE!
SHIVER
STIFF
NEXT DAY
HOO CAD I CUB OOT TAE PLAY WHEN I'B ID BY BED!
HUH! PANSY!
SISSY!

The Sunday Post 14th January 1945

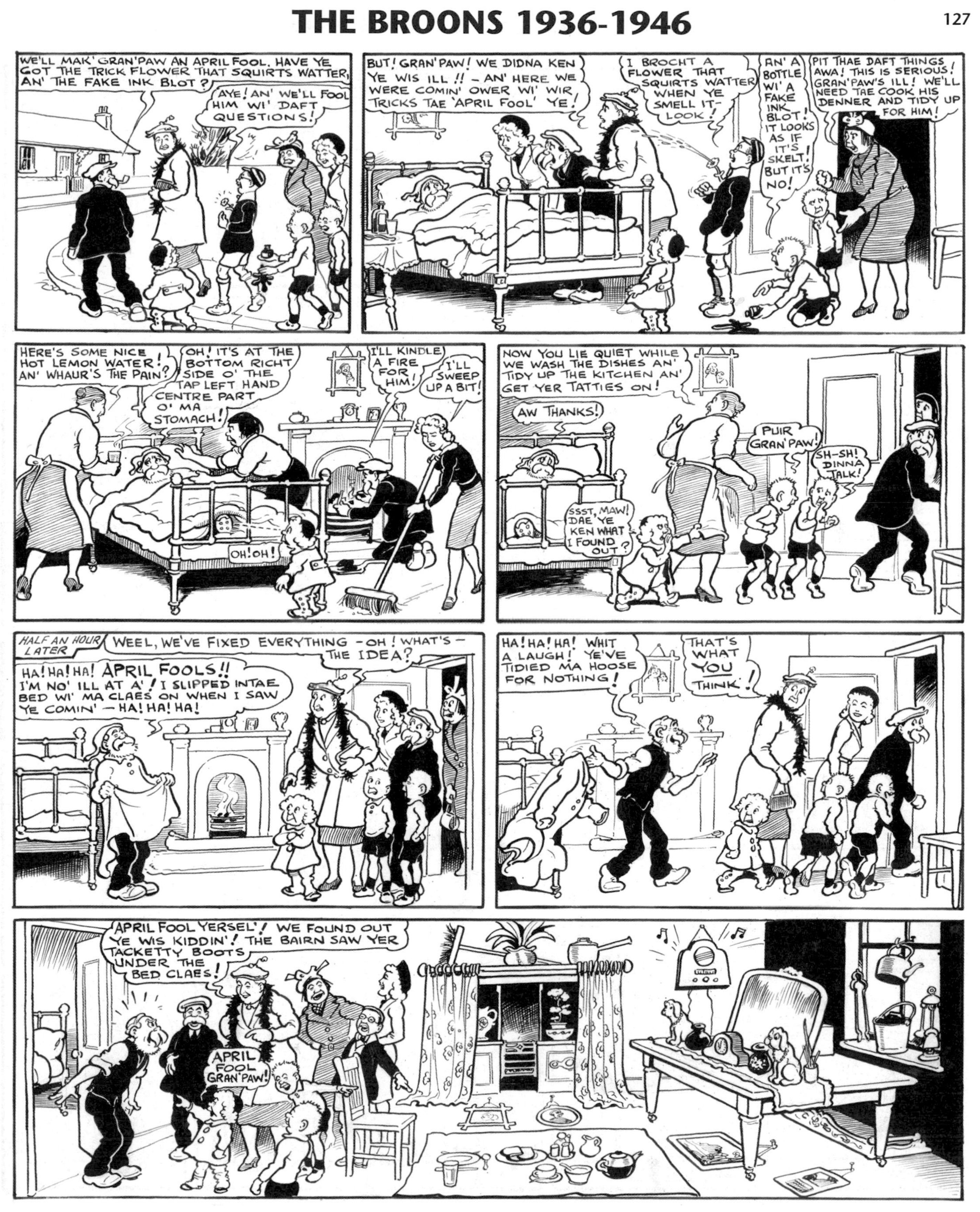
WE'LL MAK' GRAN'PAW AN APRIL FOOL. HAVE YE GOT THE TRICK FLOWER THAT SQUIRTS WATTER, AN' THE FAKE INK BLOT?
AYE! AN' WE'LL FOOL HIM WI' DAFT QUESTIONS!
BUT! GRAN'PAW! WE DIDNA KEN YE WIS ILL!! - AN' HERE WE WERE COMIN' OWER WI' WIR TRICKS TAE 'APRIL FOOL' YE!
I BROCHT A FLOWER THAT SQUIRTS WATTER WHEN YE SMELL IT- LOOK!
AN' A BOTTLE WI' A FAKE INK BLOT! IT LOOKS AS IF IT'S SKELT! BUT IT'S NO!
PIT THAE DAFT THINGS AWA! THIS IS SERIOUS! GRAN'PAW'S ILL! WE'LL NEED TAE COOK HIS DENNER AND TIDY UP FOR HIM!
HERE'S SOME NICE HOT LEMON WATER! AN' WHAUR'S THE PAIN?
OH! IT'S AT THE BOTTOM RICHT SIDE O' THE TAP LEFT HAND CENTRE PART O' MA STOMACH!
I'LL KINDLE A FIRE FOR HIM!
I'LL SWEEP UP A BIT!
OH! OH!
NOW YOU LIE QUIET WHILE WE WASH THE DISHES AN' TIDY UP THE KITCHEN AN' GET YER TATTIES ON!
AW THANKS!
PUIR GRAN'PAW!
SH-SH! DINNA TALK!
SSST, MAW! DAE YE KEN WHAT I FOUND OUT?
HALF AN HOUR LATER
WEEL, WE'VE FIXED EVERYTHING -OH! WHAT'S THE IDEA?
HA! HA! HA! APRIL FOOLS!! I'M NO' ILL AT A'! I SLIPPED INTAE BED WI' MA CLAES ON WHEN I SAW YE COMIN' - HA! HA! HA!
HA! HA! HA! WHIT A LAUGH! YE'VE TIDIED MA HOOSE FOR NOTHING!
THAT'S WHAT YOU THINK!
APRIL FOOL YERSEL'! WE FOUND OUT YE WIS KIDDIN'! THE BAIRN SAW YER TACKETTY BOOTS UNDER THE BED CLAES!
APRIL FOOL GRAN'PAW!

The Sunday Post 1st April 1945

SEEIN' WULLIE AN' BOB ARE SUCH GOOD FREENDS, IT WOULD BE NICE TAE GET A PHOTIE O' THEM!
AYE, THEY COULD LOOK AT IT WHEN THEY'RE AULDER AN' REMEMBER THEIR HAPPY BOYHOOD DAYS!
WE'RE TAE GET A PHOTIE TAKEN O' YE BAITH! THAT'LL BE FINE, EH?
AW JINGS! IT MEANS DRESSIN' UP!
—AN' GETTIN' WIR NECKS SCRUBBED!
NEXT DAY
MA SAYS I'VE TAE MEET HER AT THE PHOTOGRAPHERS! AN'—LOOK AT THESE CLAES!
MY MA'LL BE THERE TAE—AN', SHE TELT ME NO' TAE GET DIRTY!
OH, LOOK! MOTHER'S PETS!
YAH! CISSIES! DINNA GET YERSEL'S DIRTY NOW!
TAK' CARE O' YER SAILOR HAT!
I'LL BELT YER EAR! WE'RE NO' CISSIES!
TAK' THAT!
SLOSH
THROW MUD AT ME, WID YE!
HERE'S A FINE HOLE WI' PLENTY MUD IN IT!
SLOSH THEM BOB!
AT THE PHOTOGRAPHER'S
I WONDER WHIT'S WRANG WI' THAE TWA! NO' HERE YET!
WE GOT MIXED UP IN A GAME O' SOLDIERS!
OH, MERCY ME! YE CANNA GET YER PHOTIES TAKEN LIKE THAT!
IT'S ALL RIGHT, MA'AM, SEND THEM HERE TO-MORROW!
OOH! IS THAT MY BOB!
NEXT DAY
I'M GLAD WIR MA'S ARE NO' COMIN' THIS TIME! MINE'S GOT A CAULD!
AN' MINES GONE TAE SEE A WIFIE THAT'S ILL!
PHOTO
THE PHOTOGRAPHER'S TAKEN A BAD TURN SO HE'LL NO' BE ABLE TAE TAK' YER PHOTIES TO-DAY!
OH, THAT'S O.K. YOU CAN TAK' THEM!
OCH! A WEE LASSIE COULDNA DAE THAT, YE FULE!
DINNA BE DAFT! SHE'S TAE TAK' WIR PHOTIES, YE FAT SAUSAGE!
I CAN TRY!
CA' ME A FAT SAUSAGE—WID YE, WEEL, TAK' THAT!
SLOSH
SHE'S TAE TAK' WIR PHOTIES SEE?
O.K. THEN! LET ME UP!
SMILE PLEASE AND PUT YOUR HEADS TOGETHER!
3 DAYS LATER
I DINNA THINK WIR MA'S WILL LIKE WIR PHOTIE!
PHOTOGRAPHER
WE'VE GOT THE PHOTIES MA!
YES, IT'S FOR THEM TAE LOOK BACK ON WHEN THEY'RE AULDER! THEY'RE SIC GUID FREENDS!
LET'S SEE IT!
MICHTY ME!
HA! HA! HA! HAPPY BOYHOOD DAYS! HO! HO! HO!
THE PHOTIE
HA! HA! HA! PA LAUGHED THAT MUCH HE FORGOT TAE BELT ME!

The Sunday Post 18th March 1945

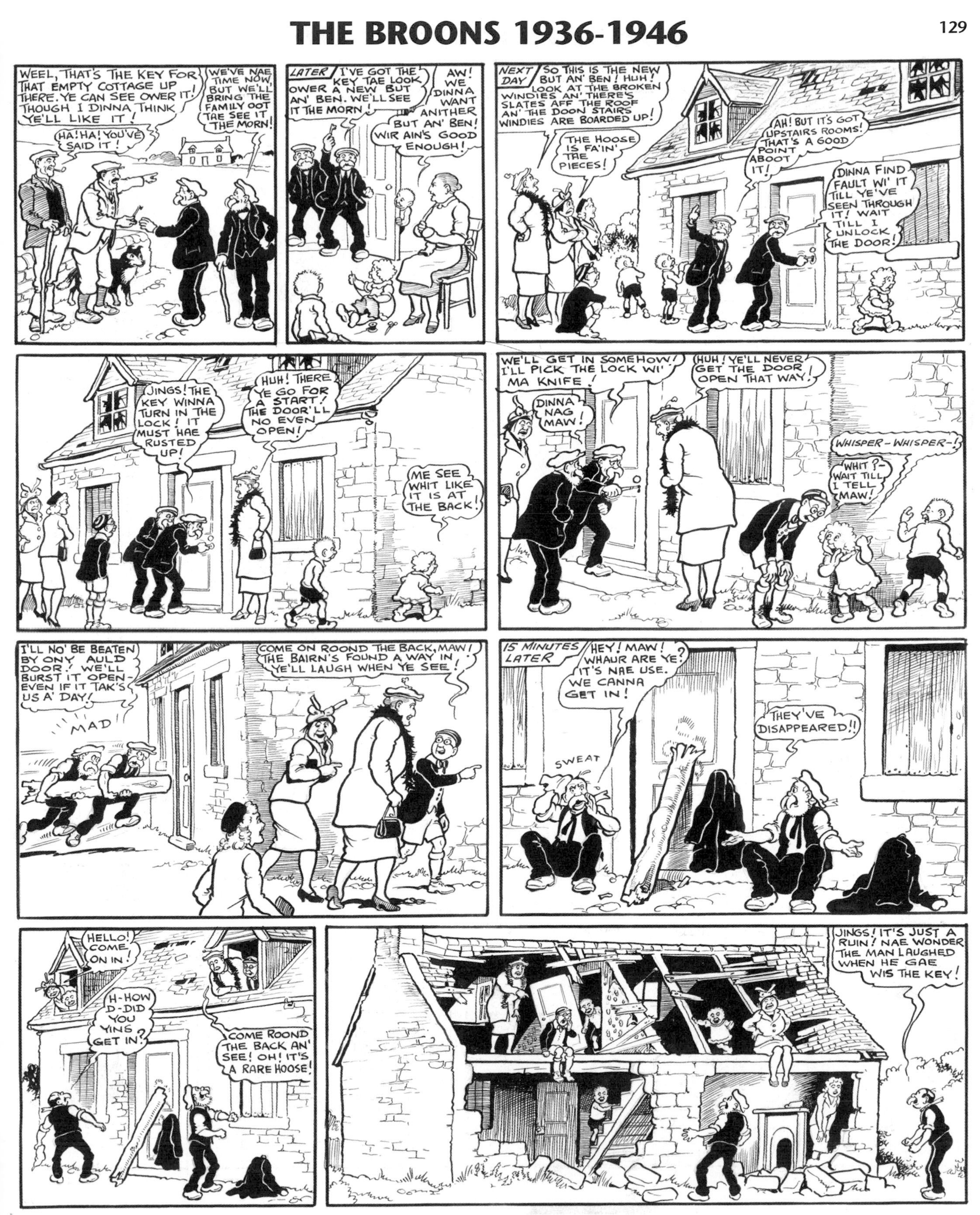
WEEL, THAT'S THE KEY FOR THAT EMPTY COTTAGE UP THERE. YE CAN SEE OWER IT! THOUGH I DINNA THINK YE'LL LIKE IT!
WE'VE NAE TIME NOW, BUT WE'LL BRING THE FAMILY OOT TAE SEE IT THE MORN!
HA! HA! YOU'VE SAID IT!
LATER
I'VE GOT THE KEY TAE LOOK OWER A NEW BUT AN' BEN. WE'LL SEE IT THE MORN!
AW! WE DINNA WANT ANITHER BUT AN' BEN! WIR AIN'S GOOD ENOUGH!
NEXT DAY
SO THIS IS THE NEW BUT AN' BEN! HUH! LOOK AT THE BROKEN WINDIES AN' THERE'S SLATES AFF THE ROOF AN' THE DOON STAIRS WINDIES ARE BOARDED UP!
THE HOOSE IS FA'IN' TAE PIECES!
AH! BUT IT'S GOT UPSTAIRS ROOMS! THAT'S A GOOD POINT ABOOT IT!
DINNA FIND FAULT WI' IT TILL YE'VE SEEN THROUGH IT! WAIT TILL I UNLOCK THE DOOR!
JINGS! THE KEY WINNA TURN IN THE LOCK! IT MUST HAE RUSTED UP!
HUH! THERE YE GO FOR A START! THE DOOR'LL NO EVEN OPEN!
ME SEE WHIT LIKE IT IS AT THE BACK!
WE'LL GET IN SOMEHOW! I'LL PICK THE LOCK WI' MA KNIFE!
HUH! YE'LL NEVER GET THE DOOR OPEN THAT WAY!
DINNA NAG MAW!
WHISPER-WHISPER-!
WHIT?- WAIT TILL I TELL MAW!
I'LL NO' BE BEATEN BY ONY AULD DOOR! WE'LL BURST IT OPEN-EVEN IF IT TAK'S US A' DAY!
MAD
COME ON ROOND THE BACK, MAW! THE BAIRN'S FOUND A WAY IN. YE'LL LAUGH WHEN YE SEE!
15 MINUTES LATER
HEY! MAW! WHAUR ARE YE? IT'S NAE USE. WE CANNA GET IN!
SWEAT
THEY'VE DISAPPEARED!!
HELLO! COME ON IN!
H-HOW D-DID YOU YINS GET IN?
COME ROOND THE BACK AN' SEE! OH! IT'S A RARE HOOSE!
JINGS! IT'S JUST A RUIN! NAE WONDER THE MAN LAUGHED WHEN HE GAE WIS THE KEY!

The Sunday Post 1st July 1945

OOR WULLIE 1936-1946

LET'S ASK TAM TODD THE TWIRP AT No12 TAE PLAY CRICKET WI' US! WE'LL MAK' HIM DAE A' THE RINNIN' FOR THE BA'!
WE'LL LET YE PLAY CRICKET WI' US! COMIN'?
OH THANKS!
WE'LL LET HIM BAT FIRST—GET HIM OOT QUICK—THEN HE CAN FIELD A' THE REST O' THE TIME!
SWIPE
TWO HOURS LATER
HURRY UP AN' BOWL HIM OOT, WULLIE!
HA! HA! YE HAV'NA' GOT ME OOT YET!
I WISH I COULD!
AW! IT'S TIME TAE G'WA' HAME FOR WIR TEA!
BUT YOU LADS HAV'NA HAD A SHOTTIE O' THE BAT YET!
NEXT DAY
WE'LL GET HIM TAE PLAY BOOLS WI' US—AN' WE'LL RUNK HIM!
JINGS! HE'S LICKIN' YE, WULLIE!
I'M RUNKIT!
THANKS FOR YER BOOLS!
NEXT DAY
OH! ARE YOU LADS GOIN' FISHIN'?—SO AM I! I'LL COME WI' YOU!
HUH! AN' WE DIDNA' CATCH A THING! I'M SICK FED UP O' THIS BLOKE! HE'S OWER SMART!
NEXT DAY
HERE! I'VE A PLAN—WE'LL ASK TAM TODD TAE COME TAE MY SHED THE NICHT—WHEN IT'S DARK! THEN WE'LL BASH HIM AFORE HE GETS THERE!
GOOD! YOU GO NOW, WULLIE—AN' ASK HIM TAE COME THE NICHT!
I'LL BE NICE TAE HIM—BUT HULLO! WHIT'S THE VAN AT HIS DOOR FOR?
OH! IS THIS YOUR FLITTIN'? ARE YE LEAVIN'?
YES, WE'RE GOIN' AWA' IN AN HOUR WHEN A' THE FURNITURE IS LOADED!
THE TWIRP'S LEAVIN'! THE FURNITURE VAN'S LOADIN' UP! HE'LL BE AWA' IN AN HOUR!
JINGS! WHIT ARE WE GOIN' TAE DAE ABOUT IT?
I'VE DECIDED WE SHOULD LET BYGONES BE BYGONES AN' GIE HIM A PRESENTATION SEEIN' HE'S GOIN' AWA!
O.K. WI US!
WE WANT A BOOK FOR A BOY! WE'VE GOT 2/2½ BETWEEN US!
WELL, HERE'S A NICE CHEAP BOOK!
WE'VE COME TO EXPRESS—ER—OOR REGRET THAT YE ARE LEAVIN' WIS AN' HAE BROCHT A TOKEN O' WIR ESTEEM TAE REMIND YE O' WIS WHEN YE ARE FAR, FAR AWA'! GOODBYE!
I THANK YE ANE AN' A' FRAE THE BOTTOM OF MY HEART—BUT, YE SHOULDNA' THINK THIS IS GOOD BYE FOR EVER!
LOOK! THE VAN'S GOIN' AWA'! YE'D BETTER JUMP ON OR YE'LL BE LEFT AHENT!
OH NO! IT'S NO' AS BAD AS THAT! YE SEE, WE'RE JUST FLITTIN' TAE—
—A BIGGER HOOSE AT No 27 ON THE ITHER SIDE O' THE STREET!

The Sunday Post 12th August 1945

MY! THE DRYIN' GREEN GRASS IS GETTIN' AWFY LANG - WE COULD DAE WI' IT GETTIN' CUT!
I'LL GET GRAN'PAW'S MOWER SHARPENED AN' HORACE AN' THE TWINS CAN CUT THE GREEN!
NEXT DAY
I'VE SET YER AULD MAN'S MOWER AN' SHARPENED IT. THAT'LL BE FOWER SHULLIN'S!
IRONMONGER
I'LL LEAVE IT IN THE WASHIN' HOOSE AN' GO AN' GET HORACE AN' THE TWINS.
HORACE AN' THE TWINS? OH! THEY WENT OOT WHEN THEY SAW YE PITTIN' THE MOWER IN THE CELLAR!
MAYBE THEY'RE AT THE SWINGS!
YE'D BETTER HELP ME LOOK FOR THEM FOR GRAN'PAW HAS TAE GET HIS MOWER BACK THE NICHT!
YE MICHT GET HORACE AT THE SODA FOUNTAIN!
HAE YOU YINS SEEN THE BROON TWINS?
NO!
HAE YE SEEN OOR HORACE?
SODA FOUNTAIN
NO! I HINNA SEEN HIM SINCE HE TOOK ME OOT LAST NICHT!
HAE YE SEEN HORACE AN' THE TWINS, P.C. MURDOCH?
NOW LET ME THINK - AYE! IT WIS AT THE - ER - NO! NO' THERE - JINGS AYE! - I MIND NOO - I SAW THEM THIS MORNIN' - OR WIS IT YESTERDAY!
AW NUTS! HE NEVER SEES ONYTHIN' - AN' IT'LL BE OWER LATE TAE CUT THE GRASS IT'S GETTIN' DARK!
MAD
WE CANNA FIND HORACE AN' THE TWINS ONY PLACE!
NOR ME EITHER! I'LL GET THE MOWER OOT O' THE WASH-HOUSE AN' TAK IT BACK TAE GRAN'PAW! IT'S OWER DARK TAE CUT THE GRASS NOW!
JINGS! THE MOWER'S AWA'!!
GONE
WHAUR HAE YE BEEN WI' THAT MOWER? DID YE NO' KEN I'VE BEEN LOOKIN' FOR YE TAE CUT THE BACK GREEN - AND NOW IT'S FAR OWER LATE! I'VE TAE TAK' IT BACK!
AYE! THEY'VE MADE A GUID JOB O' WIR GREENS!
OH! WE'VE BEEN CUTTIN' A' THE GREENS FRAE No 2 UP TO No 8! AN' WE GOT A TANNER A TIME FOR DAEIN' THEM!

The Sunday Post 5th August 1945

OOR WULLIE 1936-1946

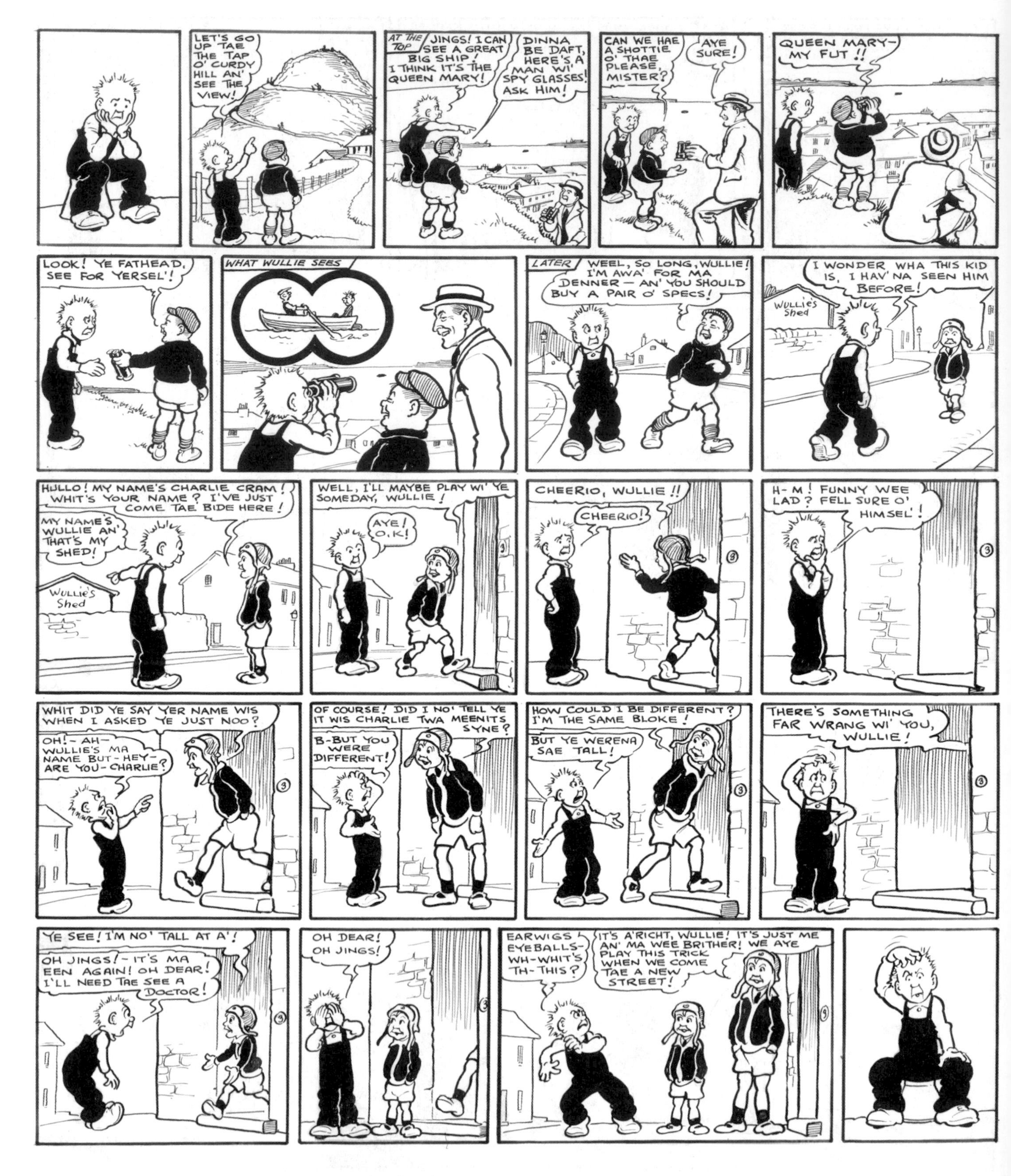
LET'S GO UP TAE THE TAP O' CURDY HILL AN' SEE THE VIEW!
AT THE TOP
JINGS! I CAN SEE A GREAT BIG SHIP! I THINK IT'S THE QUEEN MARY!
DINNA BE DAFT, HERE'S A MAN WI' SPY GLASSES! ASK HIM!
CAN WE HAE A SHOTTIE O' THAE PLEASE, MISTER?
AYE SURE!
QUEEN MARY—MY FUT!!
LOOK! YE FATHEAD, SEE FOR YERSEL'!
WHAT WULLIE SEES
LATER
WEEL, SO LONG, WULLIE! I'M AWA' FOR MA DENNER — AN' YOU SHOULD BUY A PAIR O' SPECS!
I WONDER WHA THIS KID IS, I HAV'NA SEEN HIM BEFORE!
Wullie's Shed
HULLO! MY NAME'S CHARLIE CRAM! WHIT'S YOUR NAME? I'VE JUST COME TAE BIDE HERE!
MY NAME'S WULLIE AN' THAT'S MY SHED!
Wullie's Shed
WELL, I'LL MAYBE PLAY WI' YE SOMEDAY, WULLIE!
AYE! O.K!
CHEERIO, WULLIE!!
CHEERIO!
H-M! FUNNY WEE LAD? FELL SURE O' HIMSEL'!
WHIT DID YE SAY YER NAME WIS WHEN I ASKED YE JUST NOO?
OH!- AH- WULLIE'S MA NAME BUT- HEY- ARE YOU- CHARLIE?
OF COURSE! DID I NO' TELL YE IT WIS CHARLIE TWA MEENITS SYNE?
B-BUT YOU WERE DIFFERENT!
HOW COULD I BE DIFFERENT? I'M THE SAME BLOKE!
BUT YE WERENA SAE TALL!
THERE'S SOMETHING FAR WRANG WI' YOU, WULLIE!
YE SEE! I'M NO' TALL AT A'!
OH JINGS! - IT'S MA EEN AGAIN! OH DEAR! I'LL NEED TAE SEE A DOCTOR!
OH DEAR! OH JINGS!
EARWIGS! EYEBALLS- WH-WHIT'S TH-THIS?
IT'S A'RICHT, WULLIE! IT'S JUST ME AN' MA WEE BRITHER! WE AYE PLAY THIS TRICK WHEN WE COME TAE A NEW STREET!

The Sunday Post 16th September 1945

WE'LL BRING OUR POSH OFFICER FRIEND UP THE MORN'S NICHT, MA. HE'S AWFY SWELL AN' WEEL SPOKEN — HE'LL COME O' A GOOD FAMILY — GENTRY, YE KEN!
PAW'LL HAE TAE WATCH HIS MANNERS, THEN!
NEXT NIGHT
DOES YOUR FATHER DRIVE A ROLLS ROYCE OR A DAIMLER, DAVID?
OH NO! NO! IT'S NEITHER, THOUGH HE DOES DRIVE PRACTICALLY ALL DAY!
DO YOU STAY IN A BIG HOUSE?
PINKIE STICKIN' OOT
OH NO! NOT BIG AT ALL! HULLO! IS THIS YOUR FATHER?
OH, CRIVVENS! — YES!
HULLO! WHIT'S GOIN' ON? HAEIN' A CUPPIE O' TEA? I'LL BE THROUGH IN A MEENIT — I'M JUIST CLEANIN' MASEL'!
LATER
YE'RE A DISGRACE! HERE'S MAGGIE WI' A NICE LAD WHA'S FAITHER HAS BAGS O' MONEY AN' LIVES IN A BIG HOOSE — AN' YOU - YOU - HAE TAE COME IN AN' SPOIL IT A' — WI' YER BREEKS HAUF DOON, AN' IN YER SEMMIT, AN' YER GALLUSES!
DAVID'S COMING HERE AGAIN THE MORN'S NICHT AN' IF YE CANNA BEHAVE YERSEL BIDE AWA'!
SOB
NEXT NIGHT
JINGS! I THOCHT I KENT THAT LAD'S FACE! I KEN HIS FAITHER TAM WILLS — I'LL AWA' AN' SEE HIM NOW!
PIECE
MAN! BROON! AYE — DAVIE'S IN THE ARMY — A LIEUTENANT TAE! HE'S GOT ON WELL! AWFY WEEL SPOKEN HE'S GOTTEN — BUT HE'S NO' ASHAMED O' HIS AULD FAITHER!
WEEL, COME HAME WI' ME NOO, TAM!
PIECE
OH DAVID, WE'RE AWFY — AWFULLY — SORRY ABOUT PAW — PAPA — COMING IN THE OTHER NIGHT SO - ER - UNTIDY - BUT - ER -
OH! THAT'S ALL RIGHT — YOU SHOULD SEE MY FATHER SOMETIMES!
AH! BUT WE KNOW HE'LL BE DIFFERENT! HE'LL BE SO GENTEEL!
WHY IF IT'S NO MA AIN LADDIE! I DIDNA KEN YE WIS ACQUAINT WI' THE BROONS!
OH! HELLO, DAD! WE WERE JUST SPEAKING ABOUT YOU!
PIECE
IT'S A SMALL WORLD! I'VE KENT DAVIE'S FAITHER FOR FORTY YEAR! AN' I THOCHT I RECOGNISED THE LADDIE AS SUNE AS I SAW HIM!
FUNNY THING IS, DAD, MAGGIE INSISTS THAT YOU DRIVE A DAIMLER, HAVE POTS OF MONEY AND LIVE IN A GRAND HOUSE!
SO YE CAN A' RELAX, NOW! TAK' YER JACKETS AFF, WE'RE NO' POSH AT A'. WE'RE JUIST HAMELY FOWK.
I SAID THAT DAD DRIVES EVERY DAY — HE DOES — HE DRIVES THE STEAM ROLLER!
HA! HA! HA!

The Sunday Post 14th October 1945

GRAND NEW YEAR PANTOMIME
ALADDIN AND HIS WONDERFUL LAMP
JINGS! I'D LIKE TAE SEE IT!
COSTUMES
ALADDIN PANTO
THEATRE
LIKELY GET! MA WID SAY WE CANNA AFFORD IT! HULLO! THAT'S LIKE ALADDIN'S LAMP!
YIN ON THE POSTER THAT THE GENIE COMES OOT O'!
GENIE WID APPEAR IF I RUBBED IT?
HAE A JOKE WI' HIM!
HERE I AM, ALADDIN!
TAP
TAP

1946

ACH! I'M GETTIN' SICK O' SEEIN' GRAN'PAW'S PHOTIE LEERIN' AT ME A' DAY — HIS EEN FOLLOW ME ROUND THE ROOM!
THAT'S RIGHT! AND IT'S NO' A BONNIE FACE EITHER!
AW! LET'S TAK' IT DOON AN PIT UP SOME BONNIE PICTERS INSTEAD!
AYE! AN' WE'LL HANG IT IN ANITHER ROOM!
AN' I KEN WHICH!
NEXT DAY
HULLO! I'VE JUIST NOTICED MA PHOTIE'S MISSIN' WHIT HAVE YE DONE WI'D?
AW! WE GOT FED UP SEEIN' YOU! IT'S HANGIN' UP IN ANITHER ROOM!
SEE! YER PHOTIE'S IN THE SCULLERY!
AYE! HANGIN' ASIDE THE OTHER MUGS!
OF A' THE CHEEK!
WE'LL NEED ANITHER PICTER TAE TAK' ITS PLACE!
IN FACT WE COULD DAE WI' A FEW PICTERS! THAT WALL'S AWFY BARE AN' CAULD LIKE WITHOOT PICTERS!
LOOK HERE! I'VE SOME BRAW PICTERS AT HAME, BUT SEEIN' YE'VE TAKEN MY PHOTIE AFF THE WALL, YE'RE NO' GETTIN' THEM!
IN THE HUFF
AW GRAN'PAW! DINNA TAK' ON — IF YE GIVE THEM TAE US WE'LL HANG YER PHOTIE ON THE WALL AGAIN!
OH! WEEL — MAYBE I WILL THEN — BUT THEY'RE NO FRAMED — YE'LL HAE TAE PAY FOR THAT — BUT I COULD PICK UP SOME AULD FRAMES CHEAP!
HERE'S A POUND — GET THE FRAMES OOT O' THAT AN' KEEP THE CHANGE — CHEER UP, AULD LAD!
£1
TWO DAYS LATER
HULLO! THE FOWKS OOT? I'VE BROCHT THE PICTERS — I'LL PIT THEM UP AFORE THEY GET BACK — TAE SURPRISE THEM!
AYE! AN' THEY'VE HUNG YOUR PHOTIE UP AGAIN!
FOOTSTEPS
CHATTER
HERE'S MAW AN' THEM, NOW!
AN' TAE THINK I PAID GOOD MONEY TAE HAE THEM FRAMED

The Sunday Post 27th January 1946

OOR WULLIE 1936-1946

GRAND NEW YEAR PANTOMIME
ALADDIN AND HIS WONDERFUL LAMP
JINGS! I'D LIKE TAE SEE IT!
COSTUMES
ALADDIN PANTO
THEATRE ROYAL
LAMP
BUT I'LL NO' LIKELY GET! MA WID SAY WE CANNA AFFORD IT! HULLO! THAT'S LIKE ALADDIN'S LAMP!
IT'S JUIST LIKE THE YIN ON THE POSTER THAT THE GENIE COMES OOT O'!
I WONDER IF THE GENIE WID APPEAR IF I RUBBED IT?
I'LL SHUT MA EEN, AN' RUB IT—HI! GENIE!!
HEY! LESS O' THE "JEANNIE"—
MISS TAMSON TAE YOU! TAK' THAT!
ALADDIN PANTOMIME
STAGE DOOR
HEY, YOU! EVERYTHING'S HERE BUT ALADDIN'S LAMP! WHERE IS IT?
AW-ER WEEL, I HEARD SOMETHING RATTLE DOON THE ROAD. MAYBE IT WIS THE LAMP FALLIN' AFF THE LORRY!
HATS
HEY CHARLIE! AWA' AN' FIND THAT LAMP AFORE SOMEONE LIFTS IT!
WHIT? IN THESE CLAES?—A' RICHT THEN, BOSS!
AW! I'LL SHUT MA EEN AN' GIE IT ONE MORE RUB!
JINGS! THAT LADDIE'S GOT IT!
O GENIE! I WANT A FEED! THIS IS ALADDIN CALLIN'—NAE KIDDIN'!
PUIR WEE SOWEL, I'LL HAE A JOKE WI' HIM!
VERY GOOD, HONOURABLE MASTER! ME CHARLEE GENIE. ME GIVE YOU A FEED!
MERCY ME! IT'S WORKED! THE GENIE!!
YOU COME WITH ME, BUT ME BLINDFOLD YOU FIRST!
MICHTY ME!
SH-SH!
STAGE DOOR
NAE KIDDIN' ABOOT THIS FEED, GENIE, EH?
FRUIT, CAKES, SWEETS! HELP YOURSELF O' MASTER
THANKS, CHARLEE YE'RE A PAL!
OW! YE'RE NO' A PAL AT A'! THESE ARE NO REAL—THEY'RE WAX!
HA! HA! HA!
AN' HE'S NO' A GENIE EITHER! HE BELONGS TAE GLASGOW! HA! HA! HA!
WEEL, YE SEE, THE LAMP FELL AFF THE LORRY, AN' I WENT TAE LOOK FOR IT. WHEN I SAW YOU WI' THE LAMP CALLIN' FOR THE GENIE, I THOUGHT I'D HAE A JOKE WI' YE!
OH MY!
CHEER UP, LADDIE—WE'LL GIE YE A REAL TREAT THIS TIME—YE CAN SEE THE PANTO DRESS REHEARSAL—FOR NOTHING!
OH GENIE!
HERE I AM, ALADDIN!
THE BOOGIE WOOGIE
LOOK OOT! HERE'S THE DRAGON!
OH! SAVE ME FROM THE DRAGON!
TAP
TAP

The Sunday Post 6th January 1946

ARE YE NEEDIN' ONY NEEDLES AN' THREAD? BOOTLACES?
HUH! BUYIN' STUFF AT THE DOOR!
HOO MONY TIMES HAVE I TELT YE NO' TAE BUY THINGS AT THE DOOR! YE JUIST GET RUBBISH THAT WAY!
DO NOT BE RIDICULOUS, MR BROWN!
PAY NAE ATTENTION
5 MINUTES LATER
RING!
SOMEBODY AT THE DOOR! IT'LL BE ANITHER O' THAE CHEAP JACKS SELLIN' RUBBISH! AH WEEL — THEY'LL NO' GET MY MONEY! I'LL CHASE THEM!
AH! SO YOU ARE MR BROWN! I'VE HEARD YOU'RE A GREAT MAN FOR INVENTIONS! I'VE JUST CALLED TO SHOW YOU ONE OF OUR LATEST BRUSHES!
5 MINUTES LATER
HUH! I THOCHT YE SAID YE WIDNA BUY ONYTHING AT THE DOOR!
AH! BUT SHE WISNA LIKE THAE ORRA LADS THAT COME — SHE WIS — OH — AWFY NICE!
WHIT'S IT FOR?
HALF AN HOUR LATER
OH YES, MR BROWN — I'VE HEARD ABOUT YOU BEING A GRAND BOWLER AND A GREAT SPORTSMAN — A GREAT MAN AT THE FISHIN' — WELL NOW, LISTEN!
SOFT SOAPIN' HIM!
JINGS! WHIT HAE YE GOT NOW? HUH! A BOWL O' GOLDFISH!
OH, I HAD TAE GIVE HIM SOME TRADE — HE WAS A GOOD CHAP!
A' THE AULD GOAT NEEDS NOO IS A FISHIN' NET!
20 MINUTES LATER
OH! MR BROON! WILL YE BUY THE LAST O' WIR PAPER FLOWERS — IT'S FOR THE BAZAAR — AN' WE'RE WANTIN' HAME, WE'RE SAE CAULD, AN' YOU'RE SAE KIND?
OH! MA POOR WEE LAMBS!
AW! STOW IT!
HUH! MAIR RUBBISH AT THE DOOR!
FOOTSTEPS
IT'S NO' RUBBISH! IT'S VERY GOOD — WEEL — ER — IT'S NO' BAD! OCH! I DINNA KEN — IT'S MAYBE A BIT SILLY LIKE!
YOU'RE TELLIN' ME?
MAW! LOOK AT THE RUBBISH PAW'S BEEN BUYIN' AT THE DOOR!
WHIT IN THE NAME IS THIS?
A BOWL O' GOLDFISH! AN' PAPER FLOWERS!
H-M! A FINE CHEEK YE'VE GOT — TELLIN' US NO' TAE BUY THINGS AT THE DOOR — AN' YOU BUY A' THAT RUBBISH! HOW MUCH DID IT COST?
AW — ER — 15/- BUT YE SEE!
JINGS! 15/- ON PURE DIRT!

The Sunday Post 3rd February 1946

OOR WULLIE 1936-1946

MY! WHIT A GRAND MORNIN'! SPRING'S HERE AT LAST!
I'LL PIT AWA' MA OVERCOAT AN' SCARF! WINTER'S PAST!
I'LL NEED TAE GREASE MA NEW SLEDGE AN' SKATES TAE, FOR I'M FINISHED WI' THEM UNTIL NEXT WINTER!
PIT A COVER OWER MA SLEDGE, AN' WRAP UP MA SKATES IN A GREASY RAG!
OH! HERE'S A BOOK FROM LAST SUMMER! THAT HIKER LOOKS TOUGH AN' SUN BURNT!
THE SCOTS RAMBLER
AN HOUR LATER
I'M LIKE THAT HIKER IN THE BOOK! I'LL AWA' INTAE THE FRESH, SPRING AIR FOR THE DAY!
MY! IT DOES YE GUID TAE SEE THE BUDS ON THE TREES!
OOH! THERE'S A WEE MIDGEY-JUIST LIKE SUMMER TIME!
BUZZ
OH! THERE'S A CLOUD IN THE SKY-AN' THE WIND'S GETTIN' UP! BUT IT'S STILL A GRAND DAY!
WEEL, THAT'S MA DINNER PAST. I'LL CLIMB TAE THE TOP O' THE HILL AFORE MA TEA! JINGS! A SPOT O' RAIN!
HALF AN HOUR LATER
CRIVVENS! THE WIND'S GETTIN' UP TAE!
IT MUST BE ABOUT TEA-TIME NOW, AN' BY JINGS, WHIT RAIN! OR IS IT SLEET?
AW! I'M GOIN' HAME! JINGS! IT'S CAULD! I WISH I HAD MA OVERCOAT!
CRIVVENS! HAILSTANES NOW, AN' NAE SHELTER!
RATTLE
PING
DINNA TELL ME IT'S SNAWIN'! JINGS! IT IS!
HALF AN HOUR LATER
THE SNAW'S SETTLIN' TAE! OH! WHIT A NICHT!
HAME AT LAST! AN' THE SNAW'S A FUT DEEP!
Wullie's Hoose
-BUT IT'S A' RICHT! HERE'S MA SLEDGE- READY FOR FUN THE MORN! BOY OH BOY!
MY! WHIT A BRAW NICHT! WINTER'S BACK AGAIN!
NEXT MORNING
WHOOPEE! IT'S MORNING! NOW FOR FUN WI' MA SLEDGE!
AW NUTS! HERE'S THE BLINKIN' SPRING BACK AGAIN!

The Sunday Post 10th March 1946

WHY DAE YE WANT TAE COME WI' US WHEN WE'RE GOIN' SHOOTIN?
AW! WE WANT TAE SEE YE MAK FOOLS O' YERSEL'S WI' THAE GUNS THE GAMEKEEPER LENT YE!
YE'LL NO' DAE THAT! ME AN' PAW ARE BRAW SHOTS!
HA! HA! HA!
NOW WATCH THEM MISS A' THAE WILD DUCKS!
JINGS! I CANNA HAUD MA GUN STILL!
IT MAK'S YER AIRMS ACHE HAUDIN' IT UP!
BANG
BANG
RICHT ENOUGH! THEY DIDNA HIT ONY!
WE'LL SURELY MANAGE TAE HIT A RABBIT! FIRE!
AW! THE PUIR WEE BUNNIES!
YE DINNA NEED TAE SAY THAT! THEY HAV'NA HIT ONY O' THEM!
BANG
BANG
NOW THEY'RE TRYIN TAE SHOOT PIGEONS!
BANG
COO COO
BANG
MISSED AGAIN!
WHAT POOR SHOTS! YE'VE HIT NOTHIN YET!
LOOK! THERE'S SOME DUCKS IN A POND — YE MICHT HAE A CHANCE WI THEM!
HEY! FARMER! CAN WE HAE A SHOT AT THESE DUCKS FOR 10/- ?
I'VE NAE OBJECTIONS!
THANK YE! HERE'S 10/-
IT'S MONEY FOR NOTHING — THEY CANNA SHOOT!
BANG
BANG
OH BOY! YE'VE SHOT 9 DUCKS!
COME ON! WE'LL GET THEM!
YE'VE GOT THE WORST O' THE BARGAIN! 9 DUCKS FOR 10/- ARE YE NO SORRY THAT YE LET US SHOOT AT YER DUCKS!
NO! NO! YE SEE —
— THEY'RE NO' MY DUCKS! THEY'RE HIS!

The Sunday Post 10th February 1946

OOR WULLIE 1936-1946

OH WULLIE, COULD YE TAK' MA MAN'S PIECE TAE THE JAM FACTORY?
SURE, MRS DUNCAN.
AT THE FACTORY
IT'S GOOD O' YE TAE BRING MA PIECE, WULLIE!
I SEE YE'RE MAKIN' TREACLE THE DAY. CAN I TAK' A LICK?
VAT 24
BE HERE THE NICHT AFORE 5 O'CLOCK WI' YER BUCKET AN' I'LL FILL IT WI' TREACLE
AW JINGS! THANKS!
MY! IT'LL BE A GRAND SURPRISE FOR MA TAE GET SOME TREACLE — WE'RE BAITH AWFY FOND O' IT!
AFTER SCHOOL
WAIT, WULLIE! I'VE A SURPRISE FOR YE!
SORRY! I'VE TAE BE AT A PLACE AFORE 5 — AN' I'VE A SURPRISE FOR YOU!
OH WULLIE, LEND ME YER BUCKET! MINE HAS A HOLE IN IT!
A' RICHT THEN, BUT DINNA BE LANG!
THANK YE, WULLIE!
5 MINUTES LATER
THANKS, WULLIE, I HOPE I HAVNA HINDERED YE!
YE HAVE!
GIE'S A LEN' O' YER BUCKET, WULLIE. I WANT TAE GIE MA HORSE A DRINK!
AW JINGS!
I HOPE IT'S A QUICK DRINKER — OR I'LL BE LATE!
THIS IS TERRIBLE! I'LL NEVER GET TAE THE TREACLE FACTORY BY FIVE O'CLOCK!
THANKS, WULLIE!
OH WULLIE! THE BOTTOM'S FA'EN OOT MA BUCKET! LEN' ME YOURS A MEENIT WHILE I GET MA COAL IN!
OH! WHIT A TIME SHE'S TAKIN', AN' SHE'LL NEED TAE CLEAN MA BUCKET TAE, AFORE I CAN PIT TREACLE IN IT!
THANKS, WULLIE — AN' I'VE CLEANED IT FOR YE!
O.K.! I'LL NEED TAE JUMP ON THIS BUS, OR I'LL BE LATE!
ON THE BUS
HULLO, WULLIE! I SEE YE'VE GOT YER BUCKET WI' YE!
AYE! AN' IT'S THE ONLY YIN IN THE TOON WI'OOT A HOLE IN IT!
JERK
— BUT HE DISNA KEN!
THERE'S A HOLE IN IT NOW
NEARLY 5 O'CLOCK! I'M JUIST IN TIME!
COME ON, WULLIE! HURRY AN' FILL YER BUCKET, AN' THEN COVER THE BUCKET WI' THIS PAPER TAE KEEP OOT THE STOUR!
THANKS A LOT!
MY! WHIT A GRAND SURPRISE THIS'LL BE FOR MA!
JAM FACTORY
HERE'S MY SURPRISE, MA — MY BUCKET FU' O' TREACLE!
THERE'S NAE TREACLE HERE, WULLIE — JUIST A HOLE IN THE BUCKET!
WHIT! NOW HOW DID THAT HAPPEN?
NEVER MIND, WULLIE! AWA BEN THE HOOSE AN SEE MY SURPRISE FOR YOU! IT'S FRAE AUNT MEG IN AUSTRALIA!
JINGS! FRUIT, BEEF AN' TREACLE!
TREACLE
PRESSED BEEF
SARDINES
PLUM

The Sunday Post 17th March 1946

That's the end of the first ten years for Oor Wullie and the Broon family of Glebe Street. Through the book we've seen The Broons and Oor Wullie evolve from their early beginnings to the recognisable, iconic figures we know today. It's thanks to the popularity of the strips in these early years that we still have the Broons and Oor Wullie appearing in the Sunday Post to this day.

THENK YOU
YOUR PHOTOGRAPHS PLEASE.
YOU'VE MOVED
MA GOODNESS ME !!